The Portable Stanford

published by the
Stanford Alumni Association

THE PORTABLE STANFORD is a
series publication of the Stanford Alumni
Association, featuring materials written
by some of Stanford's most distinguished
experts on today's vital issues. The PS
series is designed to bring the widest
possible sampling of Stanford's intellectual
resources into the homes of alumni.
It will include books based on current
research as well as books that deal with
philosophical issues, which by their
nature reflect to a greater degree
the personal views of their authors.

THE PORTABLE STANFORD
Stanford Alumni Association
Stanford, California

Library of Congress Catalog Card Number 74-78655

CONCEPTUAL BLOCKBUSTING

by
James L. Adams

Stanford Alumni Association
Stanford, California

FOREWORD

Few people like problems. Hence the natural tendency in problem-solving is to pick the first solution that comes to mind and run with it. The disadvantage of this approach is that one may run either off a cliff or into a worse problem than one started with. A better strategy in solving problems is to select the most attractive path from many ideas, or concepts. This book is concerned with the cultivation of idea-having and problem-solving abilities.

Since I am by training an engineer and by profession a teacher of design in an engineering school, the majority of my contacts are with people who are analytical, quantitative, verbal, and logical. These are certainly excellent traits for any problem-solver. However, so is the ability to conceptualize freely, an activity which requires a somewhat broader thinking vocabulary. My colleagues and I in the Design Division of the Department of Mechanical Engineering at Stanford University are extremely concerned with attempting to better define this vocabulary and with helping our students to expand in this direction. This book reflects this bias.

You will find nothing within about how to be more verbal or analytical, although these are both powerful problem-solving tools. Instead the book concentrates upon aspects of thinking which are useful in improving one's conceptual abilities and which we feel are underemphasized in many people's education. Although the book focuses upon conceptualization, these aspects of thinking are also pertinent in other parts of the problem-solving process. Much of the book's emphasis is on creativity, since a good conceptualizer must be a creative conceptualizer. The mental characteristics which seem to make one creative not only are valuable in idea-having, but also better equip one to find and define problems and implement the resulting solutions.

The material herein draws upon a multitude of sources. To a certain extent it represents some of the lore of the Design Division. I was first introduced to thinking about thinking by the late John E. Arnold, the founder of the Design Division, a pioneer in education, and one of my all-time personal heroes. Quite a bit of the book reflects his thinking. The overall scope of the book is somewhat the same as that used by my Stanford colleague, Professor Bob McKim, and me in various presentations to Stanford alumni and other groups. We work out these presentations together and logically should have written this book together. However, Bob has just completed an excellent book of his own, *Experiences in Visual Thinking*, which I will refer to at various times in these pages, and is temporarily down with an overexposure to writing. We therefore decided that I would put together the manuscript. Nonetheless, Bob's influence and thoughts appear throughout. Bob also had the stamina to read the manuscript, as did Professor Harold Leavitt of the Stanford Graduate School of Business, an expert in organizational behavior, Doctor James Fadiman, lecturer and resident psychologist of the Design Division, and my wife Gretchen Adams, the secret of my success. Cynthia Fry Gunn, of Bowman Alumni House at Stanford, transformed the manuscript into readable prose and selected the art work which adorns the following pages.

Thinking is not yet fully understood. You will therefore find material in this book based on unproven theory, conjecture, and non-scientific observation. Feel free to disagree with it if you would like to, because the intent of the book is not to deliver to you the last word in psychological theory. Its aim is rather to let you learn something about how your own mind works in a conceptual situation and give you some hints on how to make it work better. This is, accordingly, a "think along" book, since it is difficult to talk about thinking without observing one's own thoughts. It is also a book that will hopefully stimulate you to dig deeper into the game of thinking, with resulting benefits to your own idea-having capability.

James L. Adams

Stanford, California
March 5, 1974

"We were all wondering where you get your ideas."

Conceptual Blockbusting • v

Credits

COVER — Drawing by Jim M'Guinness. Other drawings by Jim M'Guinness are found on pages 8, 18, 19, 32, 83, 84, 96, and 97.

PAGE V — "We were all wondering where you get your ideas." Drawing by Koren. © 1972, The New Yorker Magazine, Inc.

FACING PAGE — Magritte, René. *The Thought Which Sees.* 1965. Graphite. Collection, The Museum of Modern Art, New York. Gift of Mr. and Mrs. Charles B. Benenson.

PAGE X — Escher, M.C. *Belvedere.* Lithograph. Reproduction courtesy of Vorpal Galleries, San Francisco. [Notice the peculiar pillars.]

PAGE 2 — Arnold Palmer "Athlete of the Decade" illustration. By permission of Arnold Palmer and the National Newspaper Syndicate—Chicago.

PAGE 5 — Goldberg, Rube. *Sure Cure for Nagging Wife (or Husband) Who Continually Criticizes Your Driving; Simple Reducing Machine.* Both c. 1936. Ink and watercolor. Reproduced with permission of The McNaught Syndicate, New York.

PAGE 6 — Goldberg, Rube. *Be Your Own Dentist; Professor Butts ("You Sap, Mail that Letter"); Professor Butts' Brain Takes a Nosedive.* All c. 1930. Pen and ink. Reproduced with permission of The McNaught Syndicate, New York.

PAGE 12 — Lichtenstein, Roy. *Cathedral, #5.* 1969. Two-color lithograph. Courtesy of GEMINI G.E.L., Los Angeles.

PAGES 13 & 14 (top) — Drawings from *Creative Behavior Workbook* by Sidney J. Parnes. Courtesy of Charles Scribner's Sons.

PAGE 14 — Nicholason, Karl. Volkswagen drawing from CRM Books, *Involvement in Developmental Psychology Today.* © 1971 CRM, a division of Ziff-Davis Publishing Co. Courtesy of CRM.

PAGE 24 — Paradoxical figures from *Eye and Brain* by R.L. Gregory, McGraw-Hill Paperbacks. © 1966 R.L. Gregory. Courtesy of the author.

PAGE 25 — "Three Legged Pants" illustration. Courtesy of Levi Strauss & Co., San Francisco.

PAGE 27 — Escher, M.C. *Waterfall.* Lithograph. Reproduction courtesy of Vorpal Galleries, San Francisco. [Notice the flow of water in this perpetual motion machine.]

PAGE 30 — Brahe, Tycho. *Astronomical Quadrant.* Photo courtesy of The Science Museum, London.

PAGE 34 — Seymour, Robert (Shortshanks). British, 1798-1836. *Locomotion.* Cartoon, hand-colored etching. Courtesy of The Metropolitan Museum of Art. Gift of Paul Bird, Jr. 1962.

PAGE 48 — Picabia, Francis. *Parade Amoureuse.* 1917. Oil on canvas. Collection Morton G. Neumann, Chicago. (Photo by Geoffrey Clements.)

PAGE 50 — de Chirico, Giorgio. *The Anxious Journey.* 1913. Oil on canvas. Collection, The Museum of Modern Art. New York. Acquired through the Lillie P. Bliss Bequest.

PAGE 54 — Unknown artist. 18th century. *Victorin Making His Flight.* Frontispiece of Restif de la Bretonne, *La Decouverte austrate, par un Homme-volant . . .* Leipzig, 1781. Engraving. Courtesy of Rare Book Division, The New York Public Library, Astor, Lenox and Tilden Foundations.

PAGE 59   Hogarth, William. *False Perspectives*. Frontispiece of *The Works of William Hogarth, from the Original Plates Restored by James Heath . . .* London. 1835. Courtesy of Department of Rare Books and Special Collections, University of Michigan Library, Ann Arbor.

PAGE 62   Christo. *5,600 Cubic Meter Package*. Project. 1967. Pencil on paper. Collection Kimiko and John Powers, New York. (Photo and © by Harry Shunk.)

PAGE 74   Vasarely, Victor. *Tau-Ceti*. 1955-65. Courtesy of Victor Vasarely and Gallerie Denise René, Paris.

PAGES 88 & 89   Goldberg, Rube. *Professor Butts, Training for the Olympic Games*. c. 1932. Pen and ink. Reproduced with permission of The McNaught Syndicate, New York.

PAGE 92   Christo. *Packed Chairs and Table*. Project. 1965. Collection Kimiko and John Powers, New York. (Photo by Harry Zucker.)

PAGE 102   Drawing courtesy of Walter Thomason, San Francisco.

PAGE 103   Drawings courtesy of Peter Dreissigacker, Stanford.

PAGE 111   Unknown British artist. Mid-19th century. *The Flight of Intellect*. Lithograph, G.E. Madeley, London. Courtesy Princeton University Library, Princeton. The Harold Fowler McCormick Collection of Aeronautica.

PAGE 112   Riley, Bridget. *Fall*. 1963. Courtesy of Bridget Riley and Tate Gallery, London.

PAGE 134   Adams, Gretchen. Sketch. Pen and ink.

Permission to quote material from various books was obtained from the following sources:

PAGES 60 & 61   Reprinted by permission of Walker and Company from *Put Your Mother on the Ceiling* by Richard de Mille. Copyright 1955, 1957, Walker and Company, New York. [Passage on "breathing"]

PAGES 66 & 67   Reprinted by permission of David Straus from *Strategy Notebook*. Copyright 1972, Interaction Associates, Inc., San Francisco. [Strategies and page on "Eliminate"—including redrawing of figure]

PAGES 77, 82 & 83   Reprinted by permission of William Kaufmann, Inc., from *The Universal Traveler. A Soft-Systems Guide to: Creativity, Problem-Solving, and the Process of Design*. Copyright © 1974, Los Altos, Ca., revised edition. [Passage on "Constructive Discontent" and passage on "Morphological Forced Connections"—including redrawing of "cube pen"]

PAGE 87   Reprinted by permission of Charles Scribner's Sons from *Applied Imagination* by Alex F. Osborn. Copyright © 1963, Charles Scribner's Sons, New York, 3rd revised edition. [Checklist for New Ideas]

PAGES 89 & 90   Reprinted by permission of Princeton University Press from *How to Solve It: A New Aspect of Mathematical Method* by G. Polya. Copyright 1945, Princeton University Press, Princeton; Princeton Paperback, 1971. A selection on pp. xvi, xvii.

PAGES 118 & 119   Reprinted by permission of Harper & Row, Publishers, Inc., from pages 49-51 in *Synectics* by William J.J. Gordon. Copyright © 1961 by William J.J. Gordon, New York. [A selection on Fantasy Analogy]

Special thanks are in order to both Bob McKim and Brooks/Cole Publishing Company for permitting the use of material contained in McKim's *Experiences in Visual Thinking*. Copyright © 1972 by Brooks/Cole Publishing Co., Monterey, Ca., a division of Wadsworth Publishing Co., Inc.

TABLE OF CONTENTS

CHAPTER ONE

INTRODUCTION

THE LEARNING CAPACITY of man is truly impressive, not only in terms of knowledge, but also in terms of function. The amount of information the brain can retain is phenomenal. However, so is its ability to control the actions of the juggler, the stunt pilot, or the musician. Some of the functions of man, such as circulating blood and sensing temperature, although magnificent in complexity, are automatic in that they do not require conscious learning. Others, such as running and vocalizing, are easily, almost naturally acquired, yet demand considerable conscious effort if a level of excellence is to be attained. Still others, such as tennis, leather tanning, espaliering, chess playing, hang-gliding, and reading, must be acquired through conscious effort.

How about thinking? It is certainly a most important function. Is it automatic? Is it learned consciously? The time-honored method of improving one's skill is to be continually conscious of one's performance and to seek to improve it—usually according to an ideal or standard of what is desirable. The serious golf player finds out all he can about golf and then continually practices, comparing his performance and form against an ideal. He reads books and newspaper columns on golf form and watches other more sophisticated golfers as they play.

Should the thinker act like this? Should he learn all he can about thinking and then practice and monitor his result? Should he compare his thinking with that done by more sophisticated thinkers? The common piece of Americana pictured below is part of a series designed to help golfers improve their performance.

Arnold Palmer

"ATHLETE OF THE DECADE"

ROLL INSIDE ON LEFT FOOT

The manner in which you lift your left foot during your back-swing influences the success of your over-all swing.

If you go up on the toe of this foot, as the golfer in illustration No. 1 is doing, you react in a reverse manner on

your downswing. You will lower the heel in a manner that shifts weight to the back of this foot. This could cause you to fall back on your heels.

If you roll onto the inside of your left foot during your back-swing, however (illustration No. 2), you will tend to react on your downswing by shifting your weight to the left (illustration No. 3). This is the proper weight transfer that is so necessary for consistent shot-making.

® © NAT'L. News. Syn.

Have you ever seen a similar treatment of thinking? All of us are thinkers. However, most of us are surprisingly unconscious of the process of our own thinking. When we speak of *improving the mind* we are usually referring to the acquisition of information or knowledge, or to the *type* of thoughts one *should* have, and not to the actual *functioning* of the mind. We spend little time monitoring our own thinking and comparing it with a more sophisticated ideal.

Thinking Form

There are reasons for this, of course. Thinking "form" is much more difficult to observe than, say, golfing "form." Thinking is also a much more complex function than golf. If one were to write the thinking analogue to the golf column, how could one select the "thinker of the decade" and how could one extract as simple an element as the roll of the left foot from the complex process of thinking? Yet, despite these problems, effort spent in monitoring the thinking process and attempting to improve it is a good investment for the problem-solver.

Much of thinking must and does occur in a spontaneous (unconscious) way, with little energy consciously expended in monitoring or seeking to improve the process. Let me give you an example which may illustrate this. However, before I do, let me diverge a moment and make a general comment about this book. It contains occasional examples and exercises. The content of the book is much more meaningful and much more likely to influence your thinking if the exercises and problems are worked. You can do this either alone or with other people. We have found that most of them are usually more entertaining and more successful if several people are involved. It is always of interest to see the variation in thinking among a number of people. Try the exercises on your friends and associates at whatever occasion may seem appropriate, whether they are reading the book or not. In any case, try to work them yourself. You will need only paper and pencil. It is surprisingly easy to read material about thinking, accept it intellectually, and yet not have one's own thinking processes affected. This book is a little bit like one about jogging. It won't do you nearly as much good unless you run a little.

Now, back to the example. The following puzzle, which originates with Carl Duncker, is taken from *The Act of Creation* by Arthur Koestler. Work on it awhile. When you get the answer or get tired of thinking about it, proceed.

Puzzle: "One morning, exactly at sunrise, a Buddhist monk began to climb a tall mountain. A narrow path, no more than a foot or two wide, spiraled around the mountain to a glittering temple at the summit. The monk ascended at varying rates of speed, stopping many times along the way to rest and eat dried fruit he carried with him. He reached the temple shortly before sunset. After several days of fasting and meditation he began his journey back along the same path, starting at sunrise and again walking at variable speeds with many pauses along the way. His average speed descending was, of course, greater than his average climbing speed. Prove that there is *a spot* along the path that the monk will occupy on both trips at precisely the same time of day."

A simple way of solving the puzzle is to visualize the upward journey of the monk superimposed upon the downward journey. Visualize, if you would, two monks, one at the bottom of the path and one at the top as the sun is rising. Let the bottom monk duplicate the upward journey as the upper monk duplicates the downward journey. It should be apparent that at some time and at some point on the path they will collide. This point is the spot along the path and the time of the collision is the time.

If you happened to choose visual imagery as the method of thinking to apply to this problem, you probably solved it. (A slightly more abstract approach is to imagine a plot on a graph of each monk's position as a function of time. The two lines will necessarily cross at a common position and time.) If you chose verbalization, you probably did not solve the problem. In fact, even after knowing the visual solution, if you revert to a verbal attack, the problem becomes confusing again.

Did you solve the puzzle? More importantly, for our purposes, can you remember *what thinking processes* you used in working on the puzzle? Did you verbalize? Did you use imagery? Mathematics? Did you consciously try different strategies or attacks on the problem? It is probable that you did try several methods of working the problem, but that your mind automatically switched from one to the other. You were probably not particularly aware of what mental processes you were employing as you thought about the problem. You were playing a game (like tennis) without being very aware of what you were doing or of techniques by which you could improve your game (like getting your racket back faster).

SURE CURE FOR NAGGING WIFE (OR HUSBAND) WHO CONTINUALLY CRITICIZES YOUR DRIVING

SIMPLE REDUCING MACHINE

BE YOUR OWN DENTIST!

FIRST TIE YOURSELF SECURELY TO CHAIR (A) AND WIGGLE FOOT (B). FEATHER (C) TICKLES BIRD (D) - AS BIRD SHAKES WITH LAUGHTER, IT MIXES COCKTAIL IN SHAKER (E) - BIRD FALLS FORWARD, SPILLING COCKTAIL, AND SQUIRREL (F) GETS SOUSED - IN HIS DRUNKEN EXCITEMENT, SQUIRREL REVOLVES CAGE (G), WHICH TURNS CRANK (H) AND PLAYS PHONOGRAPH RECORD (I) - SONG (J) GETS DWARF (K) HOT UNDER COLLAR AND FLAMES (L) IGNITE FUSE (M) WHICH SETS OFF CANNON (N), SHOOTING OUT CANNON BALL (O), CAUSING STRING (P) TO PULL TOOTH!

Our simple home tooth-puller by Rube Goldberg

PROFESSOR BUTTS GETS CAUGHT IN A REVOLVING DOOR AND BECOMES DIZZY ENOUGH TO DOPE OUT AN IDEA TO KEEP YOU FROM FORGETTING TO MAIL YOUR WIFE'S LETTER.

AS YOU WALK PAST COBBLER SHOP, HOOK STRIKES SUSPENDED BOOT (B) CAUSING IT TO KICK FOOTBALL (C) THROUGH GOAL POSTS (D). FOOTBALL DROPS INTO BASKET (E) AND STRING (F) TILTS SPRINKLING CAN (G) CAUSING WATER TO SOAK COAT TAILS (H). AS COAT SHRINKS CORD (I) OPENS DOOR (J) OF CAGE ALLOWING BIRD (K) TO WALK OUT ON PERCH (L) AND GRAB WORM (M) WHICH IS ATTACHED TO STRING (N). THIS PULLS DOWN WINDOW SHADE (O) ON WHICH IS WRITTEN, **"YOU SAP, MAIL THAT LETTER".** A SIMPLE WAY TO AVOID ALL THIS TROUBLE IS TO MARRY A WIFE WHO CAN'T WRITE.

PROFESSOR BUTTS' BRAIN TAKES A NOSEDIVE AND OUT COMES HIS SELF-WATERING PALM TREE.

STRING (A) WORKS JUMPING JACK (B), FRIGHTENING CAT (C) WHICH RAISES BACK AND LIFTS TROUGH (D) CAUSING BALL (E) TO FALL INTO TEACUP (F). SPRING (G) MAKES BALL REBOUND INTO CUP (H) PULLING ON STRING (I) WHICH RELEASES STICK (J), CAUSING SHELF (K) TO COLLAPSE. MILK CAN (L) DROPS ON LADLE (M) AND TENSION ON STRING (N) TILTS SHOE (O) AGAINST JIGGER ON SELTZER BOTTLE (P), SQUIRTING SELTZER ON ASH-CAN SPANIEL WHO HASN'T HAD A BATH IN FOUR YEARS. SURPRISE CAUSES HIM TO TURN THREE SOMERSAULTS OVER APPARATUS (R) AND WATER SPLASHES NATURALLY INTO BOWLS, RUNNING THROUGH SPRAY (S), WATERING PALM (T), AND SAVING YOURSELF A TRIP TO HAVANA FOR TROPICAL ATMOSPHERE.

This book aims to make you more aware of what is going on in your mind (what you are doing) and to give you a few techniques (getting your racket back faster) which may improve your capability to solve problems (the game). We will be concentrating upon *conceptualization*, or the process by which one has ideas. This process is a key one in problem-solving, since the more creative concepts one has to choose from, the better. This is true at all stages of the problem-solving process, whether one is attempting to decide upon a broad direction or implement a detailed solution.

By concentrating on conceptualization, I am not attempting to downgrade the many other processes necessary in problem-solving, such as judgment, analysis, proper problem-definition, and the critical aspect of coaxing the idea into reality. Neither am I trying to insult your intelligence by pointing out the obvious value of a rich store of concepts to choose from. However, my work with students, professional people, and others over the years has convinced me that conceptualization does not always receive the attention it should in problem-solving. Conceptualization in problem-solving should be creative and should be treated as a major activity. Unfortunately, in actual problem-solving situations, people often fall short of this goal.

As mentioned earlier, the natural response to a problem seems to be to try to get rid of it by finding an answer—often taking the first answer that occurs and pursuing it because of one's reluctance to spend the time and mental effort needed to conjure up a richer storehouse of alternatives from which to choose. This hit-and-run approach to problem-solving begets all sorts of oddities—and often a chain of solution-causing-problem-requiring-solution, *ad infinitum*. In engineering one finds the "Rube Goldberg" solution, in which the problem is solved by an inelegant and complicated collection of partial solutions. I am sure that many of you are familiar with some example of this in the form of an appliance you have attempted to repair.

Solutions To Problems That Don't Exist

One also finds the solution to a problem that does not really exist: the objects represented in the drawing (page 8) illustrate this situation. They are devices which retard the opening of solar panels for spacecraft. The two on the right were developed by an extremely competent group (of which I was a part) in conjunction with the development of the Mariner IV, which was the first spacecraft to fly by Mars. The Mariner IV was to be provided with electrical power by four solar panels, which were to be latched together during launch, and then released and opened by spring-loaded actuators. Since there is no air in space to damp the opening of such panels and since they were covered with fragile and expensive solar cells, it was the custom to use a device to retard their opening.

The object on the left of the figure is such a device which was used successfully on earlier lunar spacecraft. However, it was heavy and the designers of the Mars spacecraft did not trust it since it was filled with oil and had the potential of coating the spacecraft with a lethal layer of slime during the nine-month journey to Mars. The object in the middle of the drawing was the first solution to the problem. Unfortunately, although it contained no oil, it was extremely complex and was no lighter than the previous retarders. Its complexity and the results from a large amount of testing resulted in its rejection on the grounds of inadequate reliability.

The object on the right is the second solution. This was a central retarder which would control the opening speed of all four panels. Although it was filled with oil, the oil could not leak and the device was light in weight. However, it also proved to be unreliable as originally developed. At this point, full panic occurred in the program. There was no longer time to try a third approach, since planetary spacecraft cannot be delayed (the planet becomes much more difficult to reach until the next favorable alignment of the solar system, which usually does not occur for several years). An extremely expensive, around-the-clock emergency effort was therefore launched to increase the reliability of the damper, along with a simultaneous program of testing in order to measure the adverse effects of various malfunctions of the central retarder which might occur in flight.

One of the malfunctions investigated was that in which the retarder failed completely to retard. Amazingly enough, the results were acceptable. The retarders were not, in fact, necessary at all. It was possible to allow the panels to open free and to catch them with energy absorbers at the end of their travel. The final solution to the problem is therefore illustrated by the very *absence* of a fourth object in the figure, since Mariner IV went to Mars without retarders—the most elegant possible solution to the problem.

The moral in the story is obvious. The apparent shortage of time in the development of this project coupled with the natural desire of those involved to solve problems as quickly as possible resulted in overlooking alternate concepts (such as *no* retardation) which could have prevented the wild-goose chase.

Examples of the effects of the hit-and-run approach are as plentiful in other fields. Perhaps the most dramatic are hastily thought-out and implemented solutions which create more problems than they solve. Many examples of this have been given publicity in the environmental area and have resulted in the layers of regulation which now apply to anyone working on problems with environmental impact. This regulation will undoubtedly be beneficial, since it requires that a large amount of effort be put into conceptualization before a solution is implemented. The amount of thought which has gone into the problem of moving oil from the north slope of Alaska to the rest of the U.S. would probably not have occurred without governmental pressure. The quality of the solution should benefit from this conceptualization.

The ability to conceptualize productively and creatively is as important in painting the bathroom as in moving oil from Alaska, in taking family vacations as in designing spacecraft, and in spending a family income as in protecting the environment. Although my major interest is the design of things, I am convinced that the conceptual process is a general one and that the same problems arise in thinking up a more nutritional diet as in thinking up a better way to image the heart ultrasonically.

Thinking well (once again, like playing tennis well) requires that many decisions be made unconsciously. One can no more think well by consciously picking each strategy and writing each sentence out longhand in the mind than one can play tennis well by consciously thinking of what position to place each joint in the body as one attempts to reach a difficult shot. However, just as tennis benefits from your becoming so familiar with various strategies that they become automatic, so does thinking.

As the book proceeds, I will attempt to make you more conscious of the creative process, various blocks that inhibit it, and various tricks which can augment it. Although this is not a psychology book, some of the theory underlying creativity will be briefly explored. These theoretical explications, although interesting, are incomplete. Hence, there is no specific thinking pattern which can make everyone into a super-conceptualizer. Some techniques and approaches work effectively for some people and yet fill others with loathing. If you come up against techniques or exercises that do nothing for you, plunge on. You will (hopefully) soon find techniques and exercises which prove interesting to you.

A question which always arises when one approaches the *teaching* of creativity is "Can it be taught?" Obviously I think that it can be, or I would not be writing this book. The teaching may be more of an *encouraging*, but call it what you will, I am convinced that our efforts at Stanford result in an improvement in the quality of conceptual output from our students. Another question which often comes up is "Can't conscious efforts to be creative interfere with the creative process?" This will be dealt with more thoroughly in Chapter Four but, in brief, the answer is simple. If a Da Vinci happens to be reading this book he is probably wasting his time. However, most of us are not Da Vincis.

One of the earliest theories about creativity considers it to be a divine spark. Plato, in III, Ion, says about poets:

> And for this reason God takes away the minds of these men and uses them as his ministers, just as he does soothsayers and goodly seers in order that we who hear them may know that it is not they who utter these words of great price when they are out of their wits, but that it is God himself who speaks and addresses us through them.

However, for most of us, creativity is more of a dull glow than a divine spark. And the more fanning it receives, the brighter it will burn.

Conceptual Blocks

Let me now make a few comments about the framework of this book. Chapters Two through Five will be concerned with what we in the

Stanford Design Division call *conceptual blocks*. Conceptual blocks are *mental walls which block the problem-solver from correctly perceiving a problem or conceiving its solution.* Everyone has them. However, they vary in quantity and in intensity from individual to individual. Most of us are not aware of the extent of our conceptual blocks. These four chapters will discuss such blocks, give examples of them, and explore their causes. The blocks are closely related, as you will see when you begin to consider them. The particular scheme used to categorize them is for convenience only, and is not meant to be the ultimate morphology of conceptual blocks. Once again, please do the exercises and problems. The only way you will identify your own conceptual blocks is to try activities which are impeded by their existence.

Chapters Six, Seven, and Eight are concerned with *techniques* which allow one to overcome (or sidestep) these blocks. The final section of the book, the Reader's Guide, contains information for those interested in pursuing this subject in greater depth. A great deal of material exists on creativity and conceptualization, and most of it is accessible without a specialist's vocabulary. I recommend it as not only fascinating, but also somewhat unique in that one is simultaneously able to acquire knowledge and improve one's idea-having and problem-solving capability.

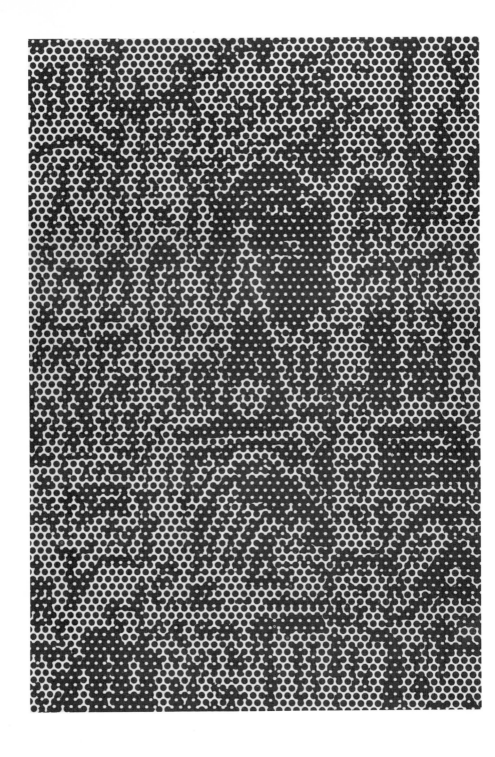

CHAPTER TWO

PERCEPTUAL BLOCKS

PERCEPTUAL BLOCKS ARE OBSTACLES which prevent the problem-solver from clearly perceiving either the problem itself or the information that is necessary to solve the problem. Perhaps the best way of illustrating perceptual blocks is to talk about some common and specific ones.

One: Difficulty in Isolating the Problem

Can you tell what the above illustration is? If you have seen this before you probably have no trouble in discerning it. If you have not, try to identify the contents before you continue.

Now that you have seen the answer, it should be easy to see the cow in the illustration on the preceding page. This is typical of visual puzzles which require the solver to detect meaning in the midst of apparent chaos.

Another puzzle such as this is the picture below. What is it?

It's a Volkswagen, of course.

Problems we face may be similarly obscured by either inadequate clues or misleading information. And proper problem-identification is of extreme importance in problem-solving. If the problem is not properly isolated, it will not be properly solved. Successful medical diagnosis depends on the ability to isolate the problem within the complexity of all of the real and imaginary information available to the physician. Successful coexistence between parents and teenage children requires the ability to isolate the real problems amongst many of the apparent ones.

Is your problem really a bad tank of gas, or does your car need timing or perhaps new distributor points? Or is your problem a living situation that makes you overly dependent upon a car? Problem statements are often liberally laced with answers. The answers may be well thought out or poorly conceived. They may be right or wrong. A problem statement to an architect such as "put a latch on that door between the kitchen and the dining room so that the door can be opened extremely easily" implies that the answer to kitchen/dining room access is a door, rather than no door, a redefinition of space, or a redefinition of the food preparation/eating function.

If one is working as a professional problem-solver, he must continually be alert to properly perceive the problem. The client, patient, customer, etc. may not always see his problem clearly, and the problem-solver is sometimes able to score heavily by curing the difficulties in a simpler manner through a clearer perception of what the problem really is. In engineering, people occasionally become so involved in attempting to optimize a particular device that they lose sight of alternate ways to alleviate the difficulty. Much thinking went into the mechanical design of various types of prototype tomato pickers before someone decided that the real problem was not in optimizing these designs but rather in the susceptibility of the tomatoes to damage during picking. The answer to the problem was a new plant, with tougher-skinned, more accessible fruit.

Problems are, of course, often constrained by considerations other than mere removal of a difficulty, and the problem-solver must be sensitive to this. Assume, for instance, that I am a consulting engineer retained to help in the design of an improved product by a company that was a leading manufacturer of mechanical equipment used to clear clogged drains and sewers. Assume further that I perceive the problem to be a general one of unclogging drains and sewers. This might lead me to a very elegant solution (a mixture of commonly available chemicals) which would make obsolete the product line of the company and which would not take advantage of the company's field of competence. Although I could then proudly take my place among successful conceptualizers, my employer would probably not enjoy paying me. Properly isolating the problem is, of course, equally (or more) important if you are both problem-stater and problem-solver. Difficulty in isolating the problem is often due to the tendency to spend a minimum of effort on problem-definition in order to get to the important matter of solving it. Inadequately defining the problem is a tendency that is downright foolish on an important and extensive problem-solving task. A relatively small time spent in carefully isolating and defining the problem can be extremely valuable both in illuminating possible simple solutions and in ensuring that a great deal of effort is not spent only to find that the difficulties still exist—perhaps in even greater magnitude.

> **Exercise:** Think of a problem that is bothering you. State your problem in writing as concisely as you can. Can you think of alternative problem statements that might be causing the difficulties you are experiencing? If so, write them down and conjecture about the possible differences in solutions which occur to you.

Two: Tendency to Delimit the Problem Area Too Closely

Just as it is sometimes difficult to isolate the problem properly, it is also difficult to avoid delimiting the problem too closely. (In other words, one should not impose too many constraints upon it.) The following common puzzle is an example of this tendency to delimit too closely.

> **Puzzle:** Draw four straight lines (without lifting the pencil from the paper) which will cross through all nine dots.

This puzzle is difficult to solve if the imaginary boundary (limit) enclosing the nine dots is not exceeded. One possible answer is shown below:

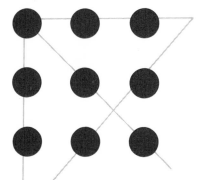

A surprising number of people will not exceed the imaginary boundary, for often this constraint is unconsciously in the mind of the problem-solver, even though it is not in the definition of the problem at all. The overly strict limits are a block in the mind of the solver. The widespread nature of this block is what makes this puzzle classic.

Such blocks are subtle and pervasive. For a talk which my colleague, Bob McKim, and I gave on the subject of problem-solving for a Stanford continuing education program for Stanford alumni, an announcement was sent out with this puzzle on the cover. An anonymous alumnus (confess) sent back the solution below:

We officially designated him/her our official conceptual smart-ass and secretly admired him because we were, of course, too blocked to realize that it wasn't necessary to draw our lines through the centers of the dots.

To add insult to this injury, one of my oldest friends later sent me the fiendish solution shown here, which allows all nine dots to be crossed off by one straight line—plus a little unblocked paper folding. Try this solution yourself—just cut out the adjoining page and start folding!

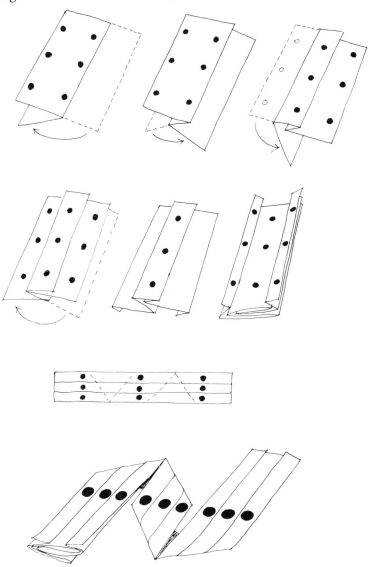

Fiendish Solution   by Rodney W. Supple

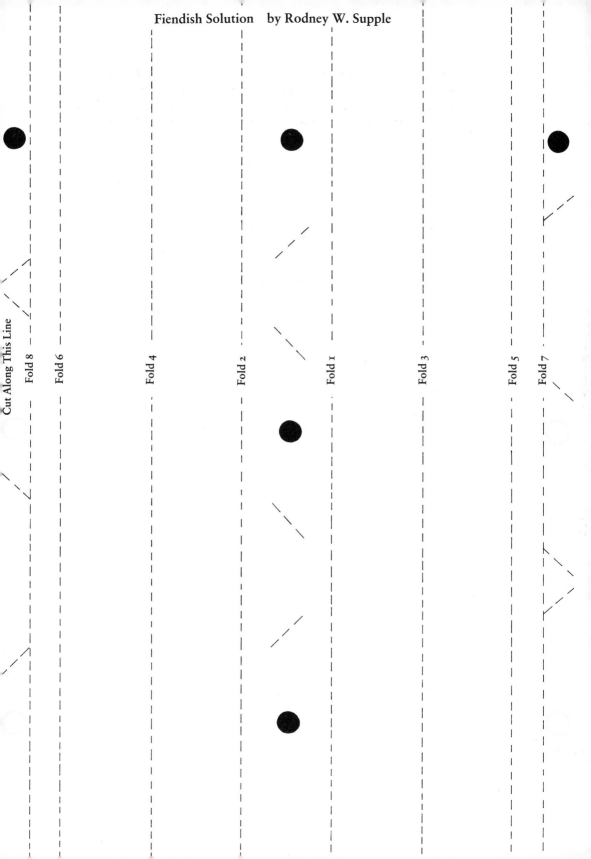

Cut Along This Line

Fold 8
Fold 6
Fold 4
Fold 2
Fold 1
Fold 3
Fold 5
Fold 7

Just as a solution is sensitive to the proper isolation of the problem, it is also sensitive to proper delimitation (constraints). In general, the more broadly the problem can be stated, the more room is available for conceptualization. A request for the design of a better door will probably result in a rectangular slab with hinges and a handle. Is this what is wanted, or is the problem really a better way to get through a wall? A request for a better way to get through a wall releases one from the preconception of the rectangular slab which swings or slides. Students given this problem statement will come up with all manner of geometries for walls and openings, elastic diaphragms, mechanical shutters, curtains, and ingenious rotating and folding mechanisms. Is this what is wanted, or is the problem a better method of acoustical, visual, or environmental isolation? The solution of a laminar air curtain as is used to keep heat in stores or out of freezers while permitting free passage would not be likely to come from a harshly delivered "design a better door" problem statement.

If you hire an architect or a structural engineer or a lawyer, you are paying for his expertise. It is therefore foolish to constrain a problem so closely ("Here is a floor plan and an elevation—build it") that you are not taking advantage of the professional's abilities. This principle applies equally if a single person is both stating the problem and solving it. A problem statement which is too limited inhibits creative ability.

It is, of course, possible to err in the opposite direction and not delimit the problem sufficiently. The resulting solution may be so general or basic as not to be useful. An automobile company looking for a better way to keep windshields clean cannot do much with a solution which does away with automobiles. The proper statement of a problem therefore becomes a critical art, since it enables the extraction of the maximum of creative thought from the solver while still delivering a useful answer. I would hazard a guess, however, that more problems are overly limited in statement than inadequately limited. Because of that feeling and because this is a book on creativity, imposing too many constraints is expressly stated here to be *verboten*.

> Exercise: The next time you have a problem, solve it. Then, at your leisure, list at least three different possible delimitations of the problem and answers you might have come up with in each case. For instance, suppose that you are in your late thirties, your children are well into school, your husband is establishing a name for himself in his profession, and you are bored.

You might formulate your problem as "difficulty in establishing contact with the real world." You might contact several people you know and find a job as a secretary for a personable and rising young star in an interesting company. After a few exciting days in your new life, ask yourself how else you might have formulated your problem, and what might have happened. Perhaps:

1. You might have considered your problem to be "difficulty in dispelling boredom during the day" (a more delimited statement). You might have taken up several crafts, involved yourself in many lunches, coffees, and volunteer activities, and attended many classes.
or:

2. You might have phrased your problem as "lack of a sufficiently challenging and productive career, now that the child-raising, home-establishing phase of life is under control" (a less delimited statement). You might then have spent a large amount of effort outlining your goals and deciding how to best accomplish them and ended up as a law student.
or:

3. You might have decided that the problem is "role stereotyping which does not result in natural fulfillment for women" (even less delimited). You might have talked to people you know, professional people, people in educational institutions, and others and decided that a large-scale social problem exists. You might have then organized a city-wide, state-wide, or even national organization oriented toward helping women, such as you, to better enter the professional world.

In engineering, as limits on problem-definition are relaxed, one usually becomes involved in interdisciplinary considerations: economic, political, and ethical. If you see your problem as simply "conforming with federal government smog regulations," your answer may be to put gadgets on existing engines. However, if you see your problem as "minimizing air pollution" you may consider entirely new concepts in transportation and will be involved in complex social as well as technical considerations.

Three: Inability to See the Problem from Various Viewpoints

It is often difficult to see a problem from the viewpoint of all of the interests and parties involved. However, consideration of such viewpoints not only leads to a "better" solution to the problem, in that it pleases more interests and individuals, but it is also extremely helpful in conceptualizing. Certainly in a problem between two people, the ability to see the problem from the other's point of view is extremely important in keeping the tone of the debate within reasonable bounds of refinement. In many cases, no solution is possible until each person can gain a feeling for the viewpoint of the other. Most problem solutions affect people other than the solver, and their interests must be considered. The architect must view the design of his buildings from the perspectives of his clients, his builders, suppliers, architectural critics, and others in his profession as well as from his own. The designer of an automobile should worry about those who must manufacture, operate, and maintain his output. The property owner building a fence must consider the viewpoints not only of his neighbors, the city council, his visitors, the garbageman, and passing motorists who can no longer see around the corner, but also of non-human participants such as his lawn, which may die in the shade of the fence, and the neighborhood cats, who may sit on his fence to better communicate their wails of war and love.

> **Exercise:** Pick an interpersonal problem which you presently have. Write a concise statement of the problem as seen by each party involved. If possible show the statements to the corresponding parties and see if they agree with your interpretation of their perception of the problem.

In his book *New Think*, Edward de Bono talks about vertical and lateral thinking. Vertical thinking begins with a single concept and then proceeds with that concept until a solution is reached. Lateral thinking refers to thinking that generates alternative ways of seeing a problem before seeking a solution. At one point in his book, De Bono explains vertical and lateral thinking by referring to the digging of holes. He states:

> Logic is the tool that is used to dig holes deeper and bigger, to make them altogether better holes. But if the hole is in the wrong place, then no amount of improvement is going to put it in the right place. No matter how obvious this may seem to every digger, it is still easier to go on digging in the same place than to start all over again in a new place. Vertical thinking is digging the same hole deeper; lateral thinking is trying again elsewhere.

De Bono acknowledges advantages in digging in the same hole, admitting that "a half-dug hole offers a direction in which to expend effort." He elaborates, "No one is paid to sit around being capable of achievement. As there is no way of assessing such capability it is necessary to pay and promote according to visible achievements. Far better to dig the wrong hole (even one that is recognized as being wrong) to an impressive depth than to sit around wondering where to start digging." However, De Bono makes the point that many holes are being dug to an impractical depth, many in the wrong place, and that breakthroughs usually result from someone abandoning a partly-dug hole and beginning anew in a different place.

Four: Seeing What You Expect to See—Stereotyping

During the late 1960s, when political activism was rampant in universities, there was a national tendency to relate hair length to personal values and political beliefs. There were exceptions to this. The leader of the Stanford conservative student society, Harvey Hukari, had long hair, much to the confusion of many. I had rather long hair at the time, and I was not only neither a conservative nor a political radical—I was even an engineer. However, the "hippie-radical" stereotyping predominated, despite any personal characteristics that might be involved. If you are a male, imagine the effect on people's perception of you if you wear a discreet, gold, pierced earring in one ear. If you are a woman, light up a large cigar. Stereotyping and labeling are extremely prevalent and effective perceptual blocks. One simply cannot see clearly if one is controlled by preconceptions.

As another example of the power of stereotyping, I wear neckties. I do not like them and at one time considered never wearing them again. However, I decided that this was a foolish battle, because the stereotyping associated with a necktie is so strong that I can accomplish things professionally much easier by wearing one, since people assume I am more important.

Perceptual stereotyping is part of the explanation for the success of various types of optical trickery such as in the figures below:

Perceptual stereotyping is not all bad, since it also allows people to complete incomplete data in many instances. However, it can be a serious handicap in attempting to perceive new combinations. Creativity has sometimes been called the combining of seemingly disparate parts into a functioning and useful whole. Stereotyped conceptions of the parts obviously hinder their combination into a new whole, where the roles they play may be quite different. Stereotyping is obviously to blame for many social and interpersonal problems. Stereotyped thinking, for instance, is a chief irritant responsible for the woman's liberation battle. It effectively impedes conceptualization, and therefore solution of problems. When stereotyping is present, judgment may not only be premature, but faulty.

Five: Saturation

Saturation takes place with all sensory modes. If the mind recorded all inputs so that they were all consciously accessible, our conscious mind would be very full indeed. Many extremely familiar inputs are not recorded in a way which allows their simple recall.

> Exercise: Without looking at one, draw an ordinary non-digital telephone dial, putting the letters and numbers in their proper locations.

Very few people can do this exercise successfully, even though they have used phone dials for a large proportion of their lives. However, the mind does not hold onto the locations of all the details of a phone dial, since it does not have to. If the letters and numbers were not marked on the phone, the mind would store the information for easy recall.

As an example of how saturation occurs at Stanford, we often ask students to draw Hoover Tower, which everyone sees many times a day and which is the butt of all manner of jokes. Few can. Like a phone dial, even though one might think that he knows the details, he cannot produce them when desired. The trickiest aspect of saturation is that one thinks he has the data, even though he is unable to produce it when needed.

Visual saturation is a problem in art schools, because it is necessary to teach students to see things they are used to ignoring. For this reason, beginning art students are sometimes told to do things like bending over and looking at the world upside down, since this upside-down orientation makes visible details which are usually not noticed (try it). Similarly if one looks away from a nice sunset one notices all manner of usually unnoticed visual activity in the easterly direction, such as colors on clouds, muted tones on buildings, reflected lights on windows, etc.

Another situation which requires attention to saturation in problem-solving occurs when data arrives only occasionally or in the presence of large amounts of distracting data. Radar inputs in the military or in air traffic control are an example of this, as are irregularities in the operation of an airplane or ground vehicle which appear after a long period of normal behavior. The life of a professional pilot, for instance, has occasionally been described as years of tedium interspersed with seconds of terror. When the information resulting in this terror becomes available, it is obviously extremely important that the pilot notice it as soon as possible. Fortunately for us passenger-types, a great amount of effort on the part of human-factors engineers, psychologists, and equipment designers goes into ensuring that the tedium will be suitably interrupted.

Six: Failure to Utilize all Sensory Inputs

The senses are interconnected in a fairly direct manner. This will be discussed further in Chapter Seven. Senses such as sight and sound and taste and smell are commonly linked. Taste is severely inhibited if smell is suppressed. Similarly sight is augmented in a major way by sound (motion pictures).

Various sensory inputs (notably vision) are important to people who

are extremely innovative. This is amply recorded in the literature. In a letter to Jacques Hadamard (taken from *The Creative Process*, edited by Brewster Ghiselin), Albert Einstein said: "The words or the language, as they are written or spoken, do not seem to play any role in my mechanism of thought. The psychical entities which seem to serve as elements in thought are certain signs and more or less clear images which can be 'voluntarily' reproduced and combined. . . . The above mentioned elements are, in my case, of visual and some of muscular type. Conventional words or other signs have to be sought for laboriously only in a secondary stage, when the mentioned associative play is sufficiently established and can be reproduced at will." Tesla, an extremely productive technological innovator (flourescent lights, the A.C. generator, the "Tesla" coil), apparently had incredible visualization powers. As described by J.J. O'Neill in *Prodigal Genius: The Life of Nikola Tesla*, it was claimed that Tesla "could project before his eyes a picture complete in every detail, of every part of the machine. These pictures were more vivid than any blueprint." Further, Tesla claimed to be able to test his devices mentally, by having them run for weeks—after which time he would examine them thoroughly for signs of wear.

Problem-solvers need all the help they can get. They should therefore be careful not to neglect any sensory inputs. An engineer working on an acoustics problem for a concert hall, for instance, should not get so carried away with his theoretical analysis that he neglects to look at a wide variety of concert halls and listen to the quality of sound in each. He must also be aware that his acoustical treatment, although successful to the ear, may overly offend the eye and, if his material choice is extreme enough, perhaps also the nose.

It is for this reason that designers sometimes will consciously deprive themselves temporarily of certain sensory inputs to make sure they have adequately recorded others. The designer of a patio cover intended to take the place of shade trees until they grow high enough in a new yard would be well advised not only to look at trees, but also to listen to them, feel them, smell them, climb them, and generally saturate himself with them for a good bit of time before starting his design. In a well-working marriage, one is sensitive not only to the appearance of one's partner, but also to the sound, smell, taste, and feel of him or her. Problems between the two are best solved by utilizing inputs from all of these senses.

Convincing students that they should use all of the sensory inputs at their disposal is one of our most difficult tasks at Stanford. University students are highly verbal (they are admitted to school that way) and are relatively less competent visually. They are not used to relying on taste, smell, or feel for problem-solving. They have mostly been posed problems that can be solved (they think) verbally or mathematically. They are not used to using sensory imagery in their thinking. This subject will be covered in more detail in Chapter Seven, so we will dwell no more on it here. Suffice it to say that failure to fully utilize inputs from all the senses is a conceptual block which is quite common in problem-solving.

CHAPTER THREE

CULTURAL AND ENVIRONMENTAL BLOCKS

CULTURAL BLOCKS ARE ACQUIRED by exposure to a given set of cultural patterns. Environmental blocks are imposed by our immediate social and physical environment. Since these two types of blocks are somewhat interrelated, we will discuss both of them in this chapter. Some examples of cultural blocks (for our culture) are:

1. Fantasy and reflection are a waste of time, lazy, even crazy
2. Playfulness is for children only
3. Problem-solving is a serious business and humor is out of place
4. Reason, logic, numbers, utility, practicality are *good*; feeling, intuition, qualitative judgments, pleasure are *bad*
5. Tradition is preferable to change
6. Any problem can be solved by scientific thinking and lots of money
7. Taboos

Some examples of environmental blocks are:

1. Lack of cooperation and trust among colleagues
2. Autocratic boss who values only his own ideas; does not reward others
3. Distractions—phone, easy intrusions
4. Lack of support to bring ideas into action

Let us discuss cultural blocks first. We will begin by working a problem that will make the message clearer.

> **Exercise:** Assume that a steel pipe is imbedded in the concrete floor of a bare room as shown below. The inside diameter is .06″ larger than the diameter of a ping-pong ball (1.50″) which is resting gently at the bottom of the pipe. You are one of a group of six people in the room, along with the following objects:
>
> > 100′ of clothesline
> > A carpenter's hammer
> > A chisel
> > A box of Wheaties
> > A file
> > A wire coat hanger
> > A monkey wrench
> > A light bulb
>
> List as many ways you can think of (in five minutes) to get the ball out of the pipe without damaging the ball, tube, or floor.

J.P. Guilford, one of the pioneers in the study of creativity, speaks a great deal about fluency and flexibility of thought. *Fluency* refers to the number of concepts one produces in a given length of time. If you are a fluent thinker, you have a long list of methods of retrieving the ball from the pipe. However, quantity is only part of the game. *Flexibility* refers to the diversity of the ideas generated. If you are a flexible thinker, you should have come up with a wide variety of methods. If you thought of filing the wire coat hanger in two, flattening the resulting ends, and making large tweezers to retrieve the ball, you came up with a solution to the problem, but a fairly common one. If you thought of smashing the handle of the hammer with the monkey wrench and using the resulting splinters to retrieve the ball, you were demonstrating a bit more flexibility of thought, since one does not usually think of using a tool as a source of splinters to do something with. If you managed to do something with the Wheaties you are an even more flexible thinker.

Did you think of having your group urinate in the pipe? If you did not think of this, why not? The answer is probably a cultural block, in this case a *taboo*, since urinating is somewhat of a closet activity in the U.S.

Taboos

We have used this ping-pong ball exercise with many groups and the response is not only a function of our culture, but also of the particular people in the group and the particular ambiance of the meeting. A mixed group newly convened in elegant surroundings will seldom think of urinating in the pipe. Even if members in the group do come up with this as a solution, they will keep very quiet about it. A group of people who work together, especially if all-male and if it's at the end of a working session, will instantly break into delighted chortles as they think of this and equally gross solutions. The importance of this answer is not that urinating in the pipe is necessarily the best of all solutions to the problem (although it is certainly a good one), but rather that cultural taboos can remove entire families of solutions from the ready grasp of the problem-solver. Taboos therefore are conceptual blocks. This is not a tirade against taboos. Taboos usually are directed against acts which would cause displeasure to certain members of a society. They therefore play a positive cultural role. However, it is the acts themselves which would offend. If imagined, rather than carried out, the acts are not harmful. Therefore, when working on problems within the privacy of one's own mind, one does not have to be concerned with the violation of taboos.

Let us discuss a few more cultural blocks. The first two listed earlier, "Fantasy and reflection are a waste of time, lazy, even crazy" and "Play-fulness is for children only," will be discussed further in the next chapter. However, a few comments should be made here. There is quite a bit of evidence to indicate that fantasy, reflection, and mental playful-ness are essential to good conceptualization. These are properties which seem to exist in children, and then unfortunately are to some extent socialized out of people in our culture. A four-year-old who amuses himself with an imaginary friend, with whom he shares his experiences and communicates, is cute. A 30-year-old with a similar imaginary

Note. In the Ladies Vehicle the Steam is made with a strong infusion of Gunpowder Tea   (*LOCOMOTION.*)   For an explanation of the Machinery see the next Number of the Edinburg Review

friend is something else again. "Daydreaming" or "woolgathering" is considered to be a symptom of an unproductive person.

As mentioned previously, environmental and cultural blocks are somewhat interrelated. People can fantasize much more easily in a supportive environment. We quite frequently ask students to fantasize as part of a design task, and when assigned the task they do quite well. However, they tend to feel quite guilty if they spend their time in fantasy if it is not an assigned part of the problem, since it often seems to be a diversion. Nevertheless, if one is attempting to solve a problem having to do with bickering children, is it not worth the time and effort to fantasize a situation in which one's children do not bicker and proceed to examine the situation closely to see how it works? If one is designing a new recreational vehicle, should he not fantasize what it would be like to use that vehicle?

Many psychologists have concluded that children are more creative than adults. One explanation for this is that the adult is so much more aware of practical constraints. Another explanation, which I believe, is that our culture trains mental playfulness, fantasy, and reflectiveness out of people by placing more stress on the value of channeled mental activities. We spend more time attempting to derive a better world directly from what we have than in imagining a better world and what it would be. Both are important.

Humor in Problem-Solving

Another cultural block mentioned was, "Problem-solving is a serious business and humor is out of place." In an essay, "The Three Domains of Creativity," Arthur Koestler, one of the more important writers who treat conceptualization, identifies these "domains" as *artistic originality* (which he calls the "ah!" reaction), *scientific discovery* (the "aha!" reaction), and *comic inspiration* (the "haha!" reaction). He defines creative acts as *the combination of previously unrelated structures in such a way that you get more out of the emergent whole than you have put in*. He explains comic inspiration, for example, as stemming from "the interaction of two mutually exclusive associative contexts." As in creative artistic and scientific acts, two ideas have to be brought together that are not ordinarily combined. This is one of the essentials of creative thinking. In the particular case of humor, according to Koestler, the interaction causes us "to perceive the situation in two self-consistent but habitually incompatible frames of reference." The joke-teller typically starts a logical chain of events. The punch line then sharply cuts across the chain with a totally unexpected line. The tension developed in the first line is therefore shown to be a put-on and with its release, the audience laughs. Let us look at a couple of jokes:

> 1. A man, on entering the waiting room of a veterinarian's of-
> fice with his sick dog, sat next to a lady with a beautiful wolf-
> hound. The wolfhound was extremely high-spirited and hap-
> pily gamboled around the waiting room, as the man's own dog
> lay limply on the floor. Finally, curious as to why such an ap-
> parently healthy dog should be in a veterinarian's office, he
> turned to the lady and said:
> "You certainly have a beautiful dog."
> "Oh, thank you," she replied.
> "He looks so healthy," said he, "that I am surprised to see
> him in a veterinarian's office. What is wrong with him?"
> "Oh," she said with some embarrassment, "he has syph-
> ilis."
> "Syphilis!" he said. "How did he get syphilis?"
> "Well," she said, "he claims he got it from a tree."
> (attributed to Dorothy Parker)

> 2. A woman at a formal dinner was quite discomfited to ob-
> serve that the man across from her was piling his sliced carrots
> carefully upon his head. She watched with horror as the pile
> grew higher and higher and the sauce began to drip from his

hair. She could finally stand it no longer, so she leaned toward him and said,

"Pardon me, sir, but why on earth are you piling your carrots on your head?"

"My God," said he, "are they carrots? I thought they were sweet potatoes."

(source unknown)

Is Koestler's explanation of comic inspiration correct? It would seem so in these two examples, since in each case a developing story (causing tension in the listener, who wants to know how it comes out) is smashed by another line of thinking which demonstrates to the listener that the whole thing is a farce. The listener then (hopefully) laughs.

The critical point of interest here is that a similar reaction (laughter) may greet an original idea. A concept may be so contrary to the logical progress of the problem solution that it may be a tension release and cause laughter. Since an answer to a problem may release tension anyway, your unbelievably insightful solution to a problem may be greeted with giggles and hoots, not only from others but from yourself.

Creative groups with which I have been associated have been funny. So are creative people I have known. Humor is present in all manner of ways. I am not suggesting that creative activity is all fun, since it is fraught with frustration, detail work, and plain effort. However, humor is an essential ingredient of healthy conceptualization.

Reason and Intuition

The fourth cultural block on our list is "Reason, logic, numbers, utility, practicality are *good*; feeling, intuition, qualitative judgement, pleasure are *bad*." Reason, logic, numbers, utility, and practicality *are* good; but so, too, are feeling, intuition, qualitative judgment, and pleasure—especially if one is conceptualizing. This block against emotion, feeling, pleasure stems from our puritan heritage and our technology-based culture. It is extremely noticeable to me, since I work with large numbers of male engineering students in situations where they must solve problems with a large amount of emotional content.

One cause for this block, which has complicated matters in the past but is hopefully dying out a little, has been the assigning of various mental activities and qualities to either the male or the female. In the past, it has been the female who was to be sensitive, emotional, appreciative of the fine arts, and intuitive. The male was to be tough, physical, pragmatic, logical, and professionally productive. Adhering to these constraints severely limits both sexes.

Abraham Maslow describes his findings about this block in his essay, "Emotional Blocks to Creativity" (found in *A Source Book for Creative Thinking*, edited by Parnes and Harding):

> One thing I haven't mentioned but have been interested in recently in my work with creative men (and uncreative men too) is the horrible fear of anything that the person himself would call "femininity," or "femaleness," which we immediately call "homosexual." If he's been brought up in a tough environment, "feminine" means practically everything that's creative. Imagination, fantasy, color, poetry, music, tenderness, languishing, and being romantic are walled off as dangerous to one's picture of one's own masculinity. Everything that's called "weak" tends to be repressed in the normal masculine adult adjustment. And many things are *called* weak which we are learning are not weak at all.

The opposite of this block also exists, of course. Many women are culturally conditioned to be as uncomfortable about many traits ascribed to the male (reason, logic, use of numbers, utility) as males are uncomfortable about "feminine" traits. Also, we find the current wave of anti-technology people who blame the technological emphasis in society for many of man's difficulties. These people believe that feeling, intuition, and qualitative judgment are good and that reason, logic, numbers, utility, and practicality are not all that exciting.

Effective conceptualization requires the problem-solver to be able to incorporate all of these characteristics—the use of reason and logic, as well as intuition and feeling. The designer of physical things must be aesthetically sensitive if the quality of our world is going to improve, whether the designer happens to be male or female. Similarly, the designer must be able to view technology honestly and without disciplinary bias whether from an art background or an engineering background. The businessman must use intuition and the social scientist must use mathematics. The man must be sensitive and the woman strong.

Left-Handed and Right-Handed Thinking

In reading the literature associated with conceptualization, one often encounters references to "left- and right-handed thinking." This is discussed particularly well by Jerome Bruner in his book, *On Knowing: Essays for the Left Hand*. The right hand has traditionally been linked with law, order, reason, logic, and mathematics—the left with beauty, sensitivity, playfulness, feeling, openness, subjectivity, and imagery. The

right hand has been symbolic of tools, disciplines, and achievement—
the left with imagination, intuition, and subconscious thinking. In
Bruner's words:

> . . . the one the doer, the other the dreamer. The right is order
> and lawfulness, *le droit.* Its beauties are those of geometry and
> taut implication. Reaching for knowledge with the right hand
> is science. . . . Of the left hand we say that it is awkward. . . .
> The French speak of the illegitimate descendant as being *à
> main gauche*, and though the heart is virtually at the center of
> the thoracic cavity, we listen for it on the left. Sentiment, intui-
> tion, bastardy. And should we say that reaching for knowl-
> edge with the left hand is art?

Oddly enough, this historical symbolic alignment of the two hands
with two distinct types of thinking is consistent with present understanding of brain function. The left hemisphere of the brain (which
controls the right hand) contains the areas which are associated with
control of speech and hearing and involved with analytical tasks such as
solving an algebra problem. The right hemisphere (which controls the
left hand) governs spatial perception, synthesis of ideas, and aesthetic
appreciation of art or music. However, this coincidence is not the main
message here, which is that the effective conceptualizer must be able to
utilize both right-handed and left-handed thinking. C.P. Snow, in his
famous book hypothesizing the existence of two cultures, *Two Cultures
and the Scientific Revolution*, separates scientists from humanists. Yet,
if one *can* separate people that clearly, then the people one has sepa-
rated are not maximizing their creative potential. The scientists who are
responsible for breakthroughs in knowledge cannot operate entirely by
extrapolating past work, but must utilize intuition, too. Similarly, the
humanists who disregard the logical are doomed to be ineffectual (even
counterproductive) in influencing social actions.

An emphasis on either type of thinking—to the disregard of the other
—is a cultural block. In the professional world in our culture, the emphasis is placed on right-handed thinking. It is easier to get money to
support right-handed thinking than left-handed thinking. More fathers
want their sons to be lawyers, doctors, or scientists than painters, poets,
or musicians. Until the culture is willing to accept the equal importance
of left- and right-handed thinking in both sexes, a large number of its
members will continue to suffer from this conceptual block.

> **Exercise:** Put yourself into a left-handed thinking mode. Stay
> away from logic, order, mathematics, science. Think about
> your feelings, beauty, sadness, the inputs that are coming

to your senses. You can probably do this better by placing yourself in a conducive environment (under a tree in the springtime, alone in your most comfortable chair). Then switch yourself into a right-handed mode by thinking of a detailed plan to make money out of one of your left-handed thoughts. Are you ambidextrous? Are you able to shift from one type of thinking to the other, and ideally to do both at once? Or are you more comfortable with one type of thinking than the other?

The block entitled "Any problem can be solved by scientific thinking and lots of money" is of course a cultural one related to the emphasis on the importance of right-handed thinking. It is also interesting, because it exists partly as a result of popular misconception about the scientific process. Science depends both upon logical controlled progress (right-handed) and breakthroughs (often somewhat left-handed). Maslow, in his essay, "Emotional Blocks to Creativity," discusses primary creativity, which he describes as the "creativeness which comes out of the unconscious, and which is the source of new discovery (or real novelty) of ideas which depart from what exists at this point." This is the force behind the breakthroughs so necessary to science. He continues by speaking of what he calls secondary creativity, which he explains as follows:

> I am used now to thinking of two kinds of science, and two kinds of technology. Science can be defined, if you want to, as a technique whereby uncreative people can create and discover, by working along with a lot of other people, by standing upon the shoulders of people who have come before them, by being cautious and careful, and so on. That I'll call secondary creativeness and secondary science.

Primary and Secondary Creativity

The present awesome progress in genetics and biochemistry (through a large amount of secondary creativity) rests upon the discovery of RNA and DNA and their functions and structures (primary creativity). For a good treatment of this primary creativity, read James P. Watson's *The Double Helix*, if you have not already. This is an intriguing book which talks about science in a way which is so contrary to many people's concept of the scientific method that it was very controversial when it first came out. It treats the discovery of DNA as a very human and very left-handed process. Watson and co-discoverer Francis Crick relied heavily on inspiration, iteration, and visualization. Even though they were superb biochemists, they had no precedent from which they could logically derive their structure and therefore relied heavily on left-handed thinking. The U.S. space effort during the 1960s was extremely impressive and exemplified the power of science—and technology based on science. However, a great deal of primary creativity and left-handed thinking was involved. Even such basic "scientific" decisions as whether to carry instruments to measure physical quantities or television cameras on the first lunar spacecraft were made in a left-handed way, since there was simply no way to make them with sheer logic. The design of the first spacecraft required a high degree of "art" (backed up, of course, by a great deal of analysis, detail design, and sophisticated fabrication and development) because there was no precedent which the designers could logically extend.

If "scientific thinking" is properly defined, it is extremely powerful for large-scale well-funded attacks on problems; however, right-handed science is only effective if based on established understanding. Right-handed science and lots of money can solve only problems which are solely in the domain of understood phenomena (a relatively small domain). Problems with social and emotional content and high complexity, such as crime in the cities, require a great deal more than right-handed science or secondary creativity.

Unfortunately, left-handed thinking and primary creativity are harder to explain, more difficult to predict, and less consistent than right-handed thinking and secondary creativity. It is therefore more difficult to write proposals which will bring support for such activities. It is easier for me to secure funding to work on the application of some newly discovered scientific phenomena (even though the potential good of the application may be small) than it is to find support for looking for a breakthrough. In the first case, the funding agency and I can be quite confident of the detailed nature of the work which needs to be done, the approximate amount of money needed, the schedule, and that I will in fact come up with something. In the second, there is no such security. The funding agency must judge me on the basis of intangibles such as my previous performance, my motivations, and my knowledge. The second is more of a gamble than the first. Support for science therefore also tends to be biased toward right-handed thinking, since most agencies handing out money must answer to someone and therefore tend to be somewhat conservative.

The "vagueness" of primary creativity and left-handed thinking, of course, also plagues those involved in the humanities and the soft sciences. Many of the soft sciences have sought to become more quantitative and rigorous in order to take better advantage of our cultural bias toward right-handed thinking. It is debatable whether this has been advantageous. Although a scientist, I am very sympathetic to the wails of those in the humanities and social sciences as to the lack of monetary support they receive from our society. At one point in my education (after I had become an engineer) I was enrolled in art school. A painting teacher I knew would from time to time tell me that I had an excellent background for painting. His reasoning was economic. He believed that many painters were hampered in the beginning of their careers by the necessity of holding down low-paying and long-houred jobs in order to support their families. He figured that I should be able to support myself by doing engineering work part-time and would therefore have time and energy available to paint. A strange observation, but perhaps a true one. It is much easier for me to find support for my life-style than it is for friends of mine who want to write or paint. The humanities and the social sciences are extremely vital in a mature society such as ours. Their importance is presently obscured by a massive cultural block.

Tradition and Change

As a final, subtle cultural block, I would like to discuss briefly the concept: "Tradition is preferable to change." In his book *Notes on the Synthesis of Form*, Christopher Alexander discusses two types of culture, one which he calls the unselfconscious culture, and one the self-conscious culture. The unselfconscious culture is tradition oriented. Traditional form and ceremonies are perpetuated, and often taboos and legends work against change. The architect in such a culture would probably serve a long apprenticeship and learn how to make the traditional buildings (the long house, the temple). When he reached a stage in which he was judged competent by his elders, he would presumably become a master and train other apprentices. The United States is hardly such a culture. Any young architect knows better than to study traditional building forms. Ours is a self-conscious culture. New religions, forms, social movements, and styles in dress, talk, entertainment, and living crop up continually. Age and experience are venerated only if "relevant," and long apprenticeships are rapidly becoming extinct. A very high value seems to be placed on innovation.

Yet, strangely enough, many individuals value tradition more than they do change. This is probably good, since in my opinion our culture has little enough tradition. However, as far as good conceptualization is concerned, such an attitude has negative effects. Motivation is essential to creativity. No matter how talented the problem-solver, frustration and detail work are inescapable in problem-solving. Unless one truly *wants* to solve a problem (for pleasure, money, prestige, comfort, or whatever) one probably will not do a very good job. Unless one is convinced that change is needed in a particular area, he is not likely to hypothesize ways of accomplishing that change.

The problem arises when individuals become so universally in favor of tradition that they cannot see the need for and desirability of change in specific areas. The true conservative, I suppose, would fall in this category. Some environmentalists lose their credibility by being totally against change in an area. If a person is truly grounded in the "good old days," and feels strongly that changes in the past 20 or 30 years have diminished rather than enhanced the quality of life, he is unlikely to be *motivated* to be a very good conceptualizer. He is culturally blocked. The person who is in favor of change for change's sake may be a more dangerous animal to have around. Yet, as far as conceptualization (the subject of this book) is concerned, he is probably in fairly good shape.

Thinking Through Blocks

Projects requiring one to think through cultural blocks are among the most popular with our students, since the blocks are so difficult to overcome and yet so obvious once they have been overcome. We often ask our students to design puzzles, games, or situations for each other which require breaking through a cultural block in order to reach a solution. One project that sticks in my mind required that a dollar bill be removed from beneath a precariously balanced object without tipping over the object. This was extremely easy to do if the bill were torn in half. However, for various cultural reasons (it's illegal to deface money, one doesn't usually tear up things of value), no one thought of this particular solution, with the result that no one could remove the dollar. Another project required that one playing card out of a deck of 52 be destroyed. Once again no one thought of perpetrating such a crime (we are a society of card players and most of us do not approve of incomplete decks of cards). Still a third I can remember was perhaps the most basic I have seen. The solution of the problem required that a number of objects be moved around a board in a prearranged sequence in order to reach the desired final configuration. It turned out to be impossible to follow the rules and solve the problem. The cultural block? Following rules! It was simple to attain the desired configuration if the rules were violated.

A less flippant situation occurs when students from extremely rigid and theory-oriented engineering schools show up to take courses from us in design. Expertise in design is somewhat different than expertise in, say, fluid mechanics. Design is a multi-answer situation and analysis is used to gain an end, not for its own sake. The teacher, although hopefully experienced in the design process and in command of the necessary techniques, is not the usual type of academic expert, in that he does not have a monopoly on the "right" answers at the beginning of the course, and in fact may not even always come up with the "best" answer. Grading becomes much more subjective and the student must take more academic risk, since the evaluation standards are less orthodox. Students from a school system in which grading is extremely important and in which the professor or teacher is an extreme authority figure, sometimes have difficulty in adapting to design courses. They are often preoccupied with "What is the answer?" and "How do I ensure that I will get an A?"—as well they should be, since their background has been exclusively oriented in such directions. The tragedy is that many foreign students from countries which need capable designers and problem-solvers suffer from such blocks. Academic risk-taking is somewhat of a taboo. Another culturally-induced difference between students from the U.S. and those from less industrially developed countries is the difference in their knowledge of, and attitude toward, machines. Students from the U.S., Western Europe, etc. have grown up with cars, motorcycles, and other such devices and are quite at home with them. Students from less industrially developed countries often have had less opportunity in their cultures to be exposed to machinery and are therefore somewhat less experienced and more inhibited in working with it.

Environmental Blocks

Let us now move on to environmental blocks. These are blocks that are imposed by our immediate social and physical environment. The most obvious blocks are the physical. Plainly the physical surroundings of the problem-solver influence his productivity. I am sure that all of you are familiar with the effect of distractions. It is very difficult to work on complicated problems with continual phone interruptions. At times even potential distractions are a problem since when one is in a frustrating phase of problem-solving, he is quite tempted to take advantage of such opportunities. Personally speaking, when involved in problem-solving I will go to heroic efforts to be distracted. Often I have to force myself out of bed at an inhuman hour in the morning to work on a problem when I am sure I can find no alternative activities available and no one to talk to. Even then, I often just sit hoping that someone will wake up and distract me.

The physical environment affects everyone. Yet, because of the individual habit patterns we all acquire, different individuals are affected differently. With regard to mental activity, some people work better in cold rooms, some in warm rooms, some in cold rooms with their feet wrapped in something warm. Some people work better to music and some in silence; some around others and some in isolation; some in windowless rooms and some in rooms with windows. Some are impervious to their visual surroundings and others are very sensitive to them.

Supportive Environments

In his book, *The Art and Science of Creativity*, George Kneller discusses some of the sometimes bizarre devices many writers have adopted with respect to their working environment: "Schiller, for example, filled his desk with rotten apples; Proust worked in a cork-lined room; Mozart took exercise; Dr. Johnson surrounded himself with a purring cat, orange peel, and tea; Hart Crane played jazz loud on a Victrola. All these are aids to the intense concentration required in creative thinking. An extreme case is Kant, who would work in bed at certain times of the day with the blankets arranged round him in a way he had invented himself. While writing *The Critique of Pure Reason* he would concentrate on a tower visible from his window. When some trees grew up to hide the tower, he became frustrated, and the authorities of Königsberg cut down the trees so that he could continue his work."

Some people may have a particular environment in which they are most effective at conceptual work of any kind. Therefore we sometimes find the all-purpose studio, in which a person may paint, write, sculpt, invent, and whatever. Another person may have one environment in which he can best write, another in which he can best throw pots, and still a third in which he does woodworking. Even though such individual differences exist, we can still say that most individuals do conceptual work best in a particular type of environment.

> **Exercise:** Take a piece of paper and list the characteristics of the most supportive possible environment you can think of for your own conceptual work (or different types of environment for different types of work). Do the environments in which you work resemble this? If not, why not? Assuming your hypothesized environment is practical for you (not the beaches of an as yet undiscovered South Sea island), change

your working environment to more closely resemble your hypothetical one. Does this make an appreciable difference on your conceptual productivity?

Although environment usually has physical connotations, the most important environmental blocks are often not physical. In fact, if anything they verge on the cultural and on the emotional. Examples are:

1. Lack of cooperation and trust among colleagues
2. Autocratic bosses who value only their own ideas and do not reward others
3. Lack of support to bring ideas into action

As we will discuss in more detail in the next chapter, conceptualization involves a certain amount of emotional risk. Change is often threatening; therefore, so are new ideas. They can be quickly squelched, especially when newly born, imperfect, and not reduced to practice. The usual response of society, in fact, *is* to squelch such ideas. There are many ways to do this. One is to over-analyze them. Another is to laugh at them. Still another is to ignore them.

> **Exercise:** Think up a new idea, maybe an invention, that sounds reasonably plausible. Maybe an electric toilet brush, or a mail campaign to convince the post office to improve its service, or anything else. Then seriously propose this idea to friends and (if you are brave) others you meet from time to time. Note their reactions. Are any, other than your friends, enthusiastic? (Are even your friends really receptive, or are they merely being polite?) This is a poor experiment since some of your ideas may be brilliant and some terrible, and this conceivably could influence the response. However, I do not think that the difference in response will be that large. If you want to improve the experiment, try both a brilliant and a poor idea on the same people.

Accepting and Incorporating Criticism

Non-supportive responses are especially harmful when they come from bosses, colleagues, or friends. An atmosphere of honesty, trust, and support is absolutely necessary if most people are to make the best of their conceptual abilities. There are exceptions, it is true. Many of the outstanding inventors I have known have been quite confident of their abilities and less dependent on support from others. One of the best of these idea-havers worked with me at one time. Given a problem he would instantly throw together a solution. These solutions were often so poorly thought out that I would almost break out in a rash. He would then happily go to the next office and receive enough criticism on the idea to send me into a depression for several days. He would then incorporate the criticism into his idea and proceed to the next office. In this way, he would literally construct a solution and usually an outstanding one. He was successful because of his ability to accept and incorporate criticism. However, people like this are rare.

Most people are not happy with criticism and, to make matters worse, are somewhat unsure of the quality of their own ideas. They therefore require a supportive environment in which to work. One of our most serious problems with students in design classes is that they hesitate to expose ideas about which they are unsure, not only to the faculty, but also to each other. Since many of their creative ideas fall into this not-sure category (naturally, since they have little else to judge these ideas by) they hesitate to reveal them. We have to convert the class (usually a listening, competitive, no-risk situation) into a friendly, non-competitive, interactive situation in which people will take the risk of exposing their most impractical ideas to each other. Competition and lack of trust destroy such a supportive environment. No one likes to expose his magnificent concept if someone is going to steal it or be jealous.

Autocratic Bosses

Bosses with answers are a particular problem in the engineering profession. Many productive problem-solvers are strong-headed. They can carry a concept through to completion in spite of apathy or hostility from others and the difficulty of finding support for a new idea. If they happen to have good judgment, they are able to accomplish noticeable achievements in a company environment and are often promoted in management. One therefore often finds that engineering managers are successful idea-havers who are stubborn enough to push their ideas through to completion. They tend to continue in this mode when managing others. Although a manager such as this can be an effective problem-solver, he is essentially operating with his own conceptual ability and an in-house service organization—he is probably not going to make much use of the conceptual ability of his subordinates. In order to maximize the creative output of a group, a manager must be willing and able to encourage his subordinates to think conceptually and to reward them when they succeed. He should, of course, conceptualize on his own. But he should do it somewhat in tandem with the other members of his group, if he is attempting to use them to their fullest. This is an obvious piece of advice that is surprisingly often ignored. Time and time again I have seen design groups operating mainly on the concepts of the group leader. Such a group admittedly can be successful if the leader is an outstanding conceptualizer and the members of the group are content to develop his ideas. However, our concern is with environmental blocks, and such a working situation is hardly an environment conducive to conceptualization on the part of the group members.

Non-Support

Lack of physical, economic, or organizational support to bring ideas into action is also another common problem. New ideas are typically hard to bring into action. A great amount of effort is involved in perfecting an idea and then selling it. Many conceptual breakthroughs in science, for instance, have taken years of work to validate to the point where they would elicit interest from others in the scientific community. A novel itself is far removed from the original thought that inspired it. Even after the idea is fleshed out into a believable and complete form, it must be sold to an often skeptical world. This may require money and time. Again, using the inventor as an example: the small inventor is at a distinct disadvantage compared to the corporate inventor because of the fabrication support he may need, the test equipment he may desire, the legal and promotional expertise he may require, and the food and rent his family will consume while he is doing his inventing. Even the best of ideas is doomed if time and money are not available to push it to fruition.

Granted, the inventor is perhaps an extreme example. Nonetheless, even a concept for a new recipe is useless without the money to buy the ingredients and the time to cook it. A concept for a painting or a drawing is similarly useless without the supplies and the time. A concept for improving a marriage (take a vacation) requires economic and temporal support. All ideas require an environment which will produce the support necessary to bring them to fruition. This support may come from your friendly venture-capital firm, your bank, your spouse, your income surplus, or any other form of patronage. Lack of such patronage is a very effective environmental block.

PARADE AMOUREUSE

Francis Picabia 1917

CHAPTER FOUR

EMOTIONAL BLOCKS

THIS CHAPTER WILL BEGIN with a game—a game which requires a group of people, the larger the better, so try it at a party. It was, I think, invented by Bob McKim and is called "Barnyard."

> **Exercise:** Divide your group and assign them to be various animals as follows:
>
> | If their last names begin with: | they are: |
> |---|---|
> | A-E | sheep |
> | F-K | pigs |
> | L-R | cows |
> | S-Z | turkeys |
>
> Now tell each person to find a partner (preferably someone he does not know too well) and to look this partner in the eye. You will then count to three at which time everyone is to make the sound of his animal as loudly as he possibly can. See how loud a barnyard you can build.

The participants in this game will be able to experience a common emotional block to conceptualization—namely, that of feeling like an ass. If you did not play the game and want to experience the feeling, merely stand alone on any busy corner (or wherever you are right now) and loudly make the sound of one of the animals.

As mentioned in the previous chapter, conceptualization is risky and new ideas are hard to evaluate. The expression of a new idea, and especially the process of trying to convince someone else it has value, sometimes makes one feel like an ass, since you are doing something that possibly exposes your imperfections. In order to avoid this feeling, people will often avoid conceptualization, or at least avoid publicizing the output.

Before we discuss specific emotional blocks, let me make a few comments about psychological theory. Although, as I stated earlier, psychological theory does not offer a complete model for explaining the conceptual process, many theories exist and have commonalities which are pertinent to understanding emotional blocks. Of particular importance are the theories of Freud and his followers and of the contemporary humanistic psychologists (Rogers, Maslow et al.).

Freud

Much of Freudian theory is based upon conflicts between the *id* (the instinctive animal part of ourselves) and the *ego* (the socially aware and conscious aspect) and *superego* (the moralistic portion of ourselves that forbids and prohibits). The motive force in the Freudian model is the id, which resides in the unconscious and is concerned with satisfying our needs. According to Freud, ideas originating in the unconscious must be subjected to the scrutiny of the ego (which may reject them because we cannot realistically carry them out) and the superego (which may reject them because we should not have let ourselves have such ideas in the first place). If these ideas are rejected, they will either be completely repressed or they will contribute to neurotic behavior because of unresolved conflict. If they are accepted, they will be admitted to the conscious mind. (This acceptance may be accompanied by anxiety, since once the ego and superego identify with an idea one can be hurt by its rejection.) If the ego and superego are overly selective, relatively few creative ideas will reach the conscious mind. If they are not selective enough, a torrent of highly innovative but extremely impractical ideas will emerge.

Since the time of Freud, his theory has been elaborated upon by his followers. A good example of this can be seen in Lawrence S. Kubie's book *Neurotic Distortion of the Creative Process*. Kubie utilizes the Freudian concept of *preconscious* in his model of creative thinking. He relegates the subconscious portions of creative thought and problem-solving to this preconscious, reserving the unconscious for unsettled conflicts and repressed impulses. In this model, the preconscious mental processes are hindered both by the conscious and the unconscious processes. As Kubie states in *Neurotic Distortion*:

> Preconscious processes are assailed from both sides. From one side they are nagged and prodded into rigid and distorted symbols by unconscious drives which are oriented away from reality and which consist of rigid compromise formations, lacking in fluid inventiveness. From the other side they are driven by literal conscious purpose, checked and corrected by conscious retrospective critique.

Like Freud, Kubie has a model of the mind in which creative thinking is inhibited by the conscious ego and superego and in which creativity occurs at least partly below the conscious level. However, neuroses play a much more villainous role in Kubie's model than in Freud's.

The Humanistic Psychologists

Although humanistic psychologists agree that creativity is a response to basic inner needs in people, they have a somewhat broader hierarchy of needs than the Freudians. They maintain that people create in order to grow and to fulfill themselves, as well as to solve conflicts and to answer the cravings of the id. They are more concerned with reaching upward and outward. Carl Rogers, in an article entitled "Toward a Theory of Creativity" in *Creativity and its Cultivation* (edited by Harold Anderson) explains:

The mainspring of creativity appears to be the same tendency which we discover so deeply as the curative force in psychotherapy—man's tendency to actualize himself, to become his potentialities. By this I mean the directional trend which is evident in all organic and human life—the urge to expand, extend, develop, mature—the tendency to express and activate all the capacities of the organism, to the extent that such activation enhances the organism or the self. This tendency may become deeply buried under layer after layer of encrusted psychological defenses; it may be hidden behind elaborate façades which deny its existence; it is my belief, however, based on my experience, that it exists in every individual and awaits only the proper conditions to be released and expressed.

The humanistic psychologists feel that the creative person is emotionally healthy and sensitive both to the needs and the capabilities of his unconscious to produce creative ideas. Like Freud's creative person, he possesses a strong ego and a realistic superego which allow him to be a prolific conceptualizer and relatively free of distracting neuroses.

We can now come to several interesting and believable conclusions, based upon our brief psychoanalytic discussion:

1. Man creates for reasons of inner drive, whether it be for purposes of conflict resolution, self-fulfillment, or both. He can, of course, also create for other reasons, such as money.
2. At least part of creativity occurs in a part of the mind which is below the conscious level.
3. Although creativity and neuroses may stem from the same source, creativity tends to flow best in the absence of neuroses.
4. The conscious mind, or ego, is a control valve on creativity.
5. Creativity can provoke anxieties.

Now I will continue with our discussion of emotional blocks.

Emotional blocks may interfere with the freedom with which we explore and manipulate ideas, with our ability to conceptualize fluently and flexibly—and prevent us from communicating ideas to others in a manner which will gain them acceptance. Let me list a few of them, which I will then discuss:

1. Fear to make a mistake, to fail, to risk
2. Inability to tolerate ambiguity; overriding desires for security, order; "no appetite for chaos"

3. Preference for judging ideas, rather than generating them
4. Inability to relax, incubate, and "sleep on it"
5. Lack of challenge; problem fails to engage interest
6. Excessive zeal; overmotivation to succeed quickly
7. Lack of access to areas of imagination
8. Lack of imaginative control
9. Inability to distinguish reality from fantasy

Fear of Taking A Risk

Fear to make a mistake, to fail, or to take a risk is perhaps the most general and common emotional block. Most of us have grown up rewarded when we produce the "right" answer and punished if we make a mistake. When we fail we are made to realize that we have let others down (usually someone we love). Similarly we are taught to live safely (a bird in the hand is worth two in the bush, a penny saved is a penny earned) and avoid risk whenever possible. Obviously, when one produces and tries to sell a creative idea he is taking a risk: of making a mistake, failing, making an ass of himself, losing money, hurting himself, or whatever.

This type of fear is to a certain extent realistic. Something new is usually a threat to the status quo, and is therefore resisted with appropriate pressure upon its creator. The risks involved with innovation often can result in real hardship. Far be it from me to suggest that people should not be realistic in assessing the costs of creativity. For instance, I spend a great amount of time attempting to explain to students that somehow the process of making money out of a commercially practical idea seems to require at least eight years, quite a bit of physical and emotional degradation, and often the sacrifice of such things as marriages and food. However, as I also try to explain to students, the fears which inhibit conceptualization are often *not* based upon a realistic assumption of the consequences. Certainly, a slightly "far-out" idea submitted as an answer to a class assignment is not going to cost the originator his life, his marriage, or even financial ruin. The only possible difficulty would arise if I, the teacher, were annoyed with his answer (and I happen to like such responses from students). The fear which is involved here is a more generalized fear of taking a chance.

One of the better ways of overcoming such a block is to realistically assess the possible negative consequences of an idea. As is sometimes asked, "What are your catastrophic expectations?" If one has an idea for a better bicycle lock and is considering quitting a job and founding a small business based upon the lock and a not-yet-conceived product

line to go with it, the risks are considerable (unless the innovator happens to have large sums of money and important commercial contacts). If one invents a new method of flight (say, wings of feathers held together with wax) the risks may also be considerable in perfecting the product. However, if one thinks of a new way to schedule his day, paint his bathroom, or relate to others in his dormitory, the risks are considerably less.

In my experience, people do not often realistically assess the probable consequences of a creative act. Either they blithely ignore any consequences, or their general fear of failure causes them to attach excessive importance to any "mistake," no matter how minor it will appear in the eyes of future historians. Often the potential negative consequences of exposing a creative idea can be easily endured. If one has an idea which seems risky, it is well worth the time to do a brief study of the possible consequences. During the study, one should include "catastrophic expectations" (assume everything goes badly) and look at the result. By doing this, it will become apparent whether you want to take the risk or not.

> **Exercise:** Next time you are having difficulty deciding whether to push a "creative" idea, write a short (two-page) "catastrophic expectations" report. In it detail as well as you can precisely what would happen to you *if everything went wrong.* By making such information explicit and facing it, you swap your analytical capability for your fear of failure—a good trade.

No Appetite for Chaos

The fear of making a mistake is, of course, rooted in insecurity, which most people suffer from to some extent. Such insecurities are also responsible for the next emotional block, the "Inability to tolerate ambiguity; overriding desire for order; 'no appetite for chaos.' " Once again, some element of this block is rational. I am not suggesting that in order to be creative one should shun order and live in a totally chaotic situation. I am talking more of an excessive fondness for order in all things. The solution of a complex problem is a messy process. Rigorous and logical techniques are often necessary, but not sufficient. One must usually wallow in misleading and ill-fitting data, hazy and difficult-to-test concepts, opinions, values, and other such untidy quantities. In a sense, problem-solving is *bringing order to chaos.* A desire for order is therefore necessary. However, the ability to tolerate chaos is a must.

We all know compulsive people, those who must have everything always in its place and who become quite upset if the order of their physical lives is violated. If this trait carries over into a person's mental process, he is severely impaired in his ability to work with certain types of problems. One reason for extreme ordering of the physical environment is efficiency. Another may be the aesthetic satisfaction of precise physical relationships. However, another reason is insecurity. If one's underwear is precisely folded and "dressed right," one has precise control over one's underwear, and thus there is one less thing out of control to be threatening. I do not actually care how your underwear is stored. However, if your thoughts are precisely folded and dressed right you are probably a fairly limited problem-solver. The process of bringing widely disparate thoughts together cannot work too well because your mind is not going to allow widely disparate thoughts to coexist long enough to combine.

Judging Rather than Generating Ideas

The next emotional block, the "Preference for judging ideas, rather than generating them," is also the "safe" way to go. Judgment, criticism, tough-mindedness, and practicality are of course essential in problem-solving. However, if applied too early or too indiscriminately in the problem-solving process, they are extremely detrimental to conceptualization. In the Design Division, we often speak of analysis, judgment, and synthesis as three distinct types of thinking. In *analysis*, there is usually a right answer. I am an engineer: if you pay me to tell you how large a beam is needed to hold up a patio roof, you rightly expect *the* answer. Fortunately, I know how to analyze such things mathematically and can give it to you. *Judgment* is generally used in a problem where there are several answers and one must be chosen. A court case (the Angela Davis trial) is a good example. A situation such as Watergate is another. Judgments are made by sensible people as to guilt or innocence, and the situation is sufficiently complex that disagreements can occur. *Synthesis* is even more of a multi-answer situation. A design problem (design a better way to serve ice cream) has an infinitude of answers, and there are few rigorous techniques to help in deciding between them.

If one analyzes or judges too early in the problem-solving process, he will reject many ideas. This is detrimental for two reasons. First of all, newly formed ideas are fragile and imperfect—they need time to mature and acquire the detail needed to make them believable. Secondly, as we will discuss later, ideas often lead to other ideas. Many techniques of conceptualization, such as brainstorming, depend for their effectiveness on maintaining "way-out" ideas long enough to let them mature and spawn other more realistic ideas. It is sometimes difficult to hold onto such ideas because people generally do not want to be suspected of harboring impractical thoughts. However, in conceptualization one should not judge too quickly.

The judgment of ideas, unfortunately, is an extremely popular and rewarded pastime. One finds more newspaper space devoted to judgment (critic columns, political analyses, editorials, etc.) than to the *creation* of ideas. In the university, much scholarship is devoted to judgment, rather than creativity. One finds that people who heap negative criticism upon all ideas they encounter are often heralded for their practical sense and sophistication. Bad-mouthing everyone else's concepts is in fact a cheap way to attempt to demonstrate your own mental superiority.

If you are a professional idea-haver, your criticism tends to be somewhat more friendly. Professional designers are often much more receptive to the ideas of our students than non-design oriented faculty members. Professional problem-solvers have a working understanding of the difficulty in having ideas and a respect for ideas, even if they are flawed. If you are a compulsive idea-judger you should realize that this is a habit which may exclude ideas from your own mind before they have had time to bear fruit. You are taking little risk (unless you are excluding ideas that could benefit you) and are perhaps feeding your ego somewhat with the thrill of being able to judge the outputs of others, but you are sacrificing some of your own creative potential.

Inability to Incubate

The "Inability to relax, incubate, and 'sleep on it' " is also a somewhat common emotional block. There is general agreement that the unconscious plays an extremely important role in problem-solving. Everyone has had the experience of having the answer to a problem suddenly occur in his mind. One maddeningly familiar phenomenon to many people is a late answer to an important problem. One may work for days or weeks on a problem, complete it, and go on to other activities. Then, at some seemingly random point in time, a better answer "appears." Since the original problem was probably completed in order to reach a deadline, this "better" answer often only serves to annoy one that he did not think of it sooner. This better answer came straight from the unconscious as a result of the "incubation" process it was going through. I have found in my own case that this "incubation" process works and is reliable. I have the confidence to think hard about a problem (charging up my unconscious) and then forget about it for a period of time. When I begin work on it again, new answers are usually present.

Many "symptoms" of incubation are common. There is a widespread belief among students that they do their best work just before deadlines. If, in fact, they worked on the material when they received it long enough to store the data in their unconscious, then incubation can occur, and a better solution may emerge at a later time. Incubation does often seem to produce the right answer at the appropriate time. Students often claim to have come up with a winning idea the morning that it is due, after struggling futilely with the problem for days.

One must allow the unconscious to struggle with problems. Incubation is important in problem-solving. It is poor planning not to allow adequate time for incubation in the solution of an important problem. It is also important to be able to relax in the midst of problem-solving. One's overall compulsiveness is less fanatical when he is relaxed, and the mind is more likely to deal with seemingly "silly" combinations of thoughts. If one is never relaxed, his mind is usually on guard against non-serious activities, with resulting difficulties in the type of thinking necessary for fluent and flexible conceptualization.

Lack of Challenge and Excessive Zeal

"Lack of challenge" and "excessive zeal" are opposite villains. One cannot do his best on a problem unless he is motivated. Professional problem-solvers learn to be motivated somewhat by money and future work which may come their way if they succeed. However, challenge must be present for at least some of the time, or the process ceases to be rewarding. On the other hand, an excessive motivation to succeed, especially to succeed quickly, can inhibit the creative process. The tortoise-and-the-hare phenomenon is often apparent in problem-solving. The person who thinks up the simple elegant solution, although he may take longer in doing so, often wins. As in the race, the tortoise depends upon an inconsistent performance from the rabbit. And if the rabbit spends so little time on conceptualization that he merely chooses the first answers that occur, such inconsistency is almost guaranteed.

Reality and Fantasy

"Lack of access to areas of imagination," "Lack of imaginative control," and "Inability to distinguish reality from fantasy" will be discussed

in more detail in Chapter Seven In brief, the imagination attempts to create objects and events. The creative person needs to be able to control his imagination and needs complete access to it. If all senses are not represented (not only sight, but also sound, smell, taste, and touch) his imagination cannot serve him as well as it otherwise could. All senses need representation not only because problems involving all senses can be attacked, but also because imagery is more powerful if they are all called upon. If one thinks purely verbally, for instance, there will be little imagery available for the solving of problems concerning shapes and forms. If visual imagery is also present, the imagination will be much more useful, but still not as potent as if the other senses are also present. One can usually imagine a ball park much more vividly if one is able to recall the smell of the grass, the taste of the peanuts and beer, the feel of the seats and the sunshine, and the sounds of the crowd.

The creative person must be able not only to vividly form complete images, but also to manipulate them. Creativity requires the *manipulation* and *recombination* of experience. An imagination which cannot manipulate experience is limiting to the conceptualizer. One should be able to imagine a volcano being born in his ball park, or an airplane landing in it, or the ball park shrinking as the grass simultaneously turns purple, if one is to make maximum use of his imagination. Chapter Seven will contain some exercises to allow you to gauge your ability to control your imagination as well as discussions on how to strengthen the "mental muscle" used in imagining.

"The inability to distinguish reality from fantasy" is a more unusual, but equally severe, block. The creative person needs the ability to fantasize freely and vividly. Yet, if his fantasies become too realistic, they may be less controllable. If you cannot go through the following exercise without a sense of acute physical discomfort, you may have difficulty distinguishing reality from fantasy. This exercise is taken from *Put Your Mother on the Ceiling* by Richard de Mille. Stay with each fantasy (marked off by slashes) until you have it fully formed in your imagination. This game is called *breathing*.

> Let us imagine that we have a goldfish in front of us. Have the fish swim around. / Have the fish swim into your mouth. / Take a deep breath and have the fish go down into your lungs, into your chest. / Have the fish swim around in there. / Let out your breath and have the fish swim out into the room again. /
>
> Now breathe in a lot of tiny goldfish. / Have them swim around in your chest. / Breathe them all out again. /
>
> Let's see what kind of things you can breathe in and out of

your chest. / Breathe in a lot of rose petals. / Breathe them out again. / Breathe in a lot of water. / Have it gurgling in your chest. / Breathe it out again. / Breathe in a lot of dry leaves. / Have them blowing around in your chest. / Breathe them out again. / Breathe in a lot of raindrops. / Have them pattering in your chest. / Breathe them out again. / Breathe in a lot of sand. / Have it blowing around in your chest. / Breathe it out again. / Breathe in a lot of little firecrackers. / Have them all popping in your chest. / Breathe out the smoke and bits of them that are left. / Breathe in a lot of little lions. / Have them all roaring in your chest. / Breathe them out again. /

Breathe in some fire. / Have it burning and crackling in your chest. / Breathe it out again. / Breathe in some logs of wood. / Set fire to them in your chest. / Have them roaring as they burn up. / Breathe out the smoke and ashes. /

Have a big tree in front of you. / Breathe fire on the tree and burn it all up. / Have an old castle in front of you. / Breathe fire on the castle and have it fall down. / Have an ocean in front of you. / Breathe fire on the ocean and dry it up. /

What would you like to breathe in now? / All right. / Now what? / All right. / What would you like to burn up by breathing fire on it? / All right. /

Be a fish. / Be in the ocean. / Breathe the water of the ocean, in and out. / How do you like that? / Be a bird. / Be high in the air. / Breathe the cold air, in and out. / How do you like that? / Be a camel. / Be on the desert. / Breathe the hot wind of the desert, in and out. / How does that feel? / Be an old-fashioned steam locomotive. / Breathe out steam and smoke all over everything. / How is that? / Be a stone. / Don't breathe. / How do you like that? / Be a boy (girl). / Breathe the air of this room, in and out. How do you like that?

It would certainly be uncomfortable to inhale sand. Whether you can imagine the feeling of inhaling sand depends somewhat upon your ability to fantasize. No danger exists from imagining such an act, and any pain felt is imagined, not real. However, if one's fantasies are confused with reality, it can be very difficult to fantasize such things. The imagination is extremely powerful because it can go beyond reality. But in order to do this, the imagination must be set free of the constraints placed upon *real* acts and events.

VUE FROM SPOHRPLATZ ~ - FRIEDRICHSPLATZ - "Documenta" Christo 1967
PROJET POUR MONUMENTAL EMPAQUETAGE POUR DOCUMENTA 1968
THE TOP THREE MAGUETTE PAGE (colours with HELium)

CHAPTER FIVE

INTELLECTUAL AND EXPRESSIVE BLOCKS

INTELLECTUAL BLOCKS RESULT in an inefficient choice of mental tactics or a shortage of intellectual ammunition. Expressive blocks inhibit one's vital ability to communicate ideas—not only to others, but to oneself as well. Let us look at the following blocks:

1. Solving the problem using an incorrect language (verbal, mathematical, visual) — as in trying to solve a problem mathematically when it can more easily be accomplished visually
2. Inflexible or inadequate use of intellectual problem-solving strategies
3. Lack of, or incorrect, information
4. Inadequate language skill to express and record ideas (verbally, musically, visually, etc.)

A few examples should help us understand these blocks better. The monk puzzle described in the first chapter of this book is one in which choosing the correct language (visual) leads one rapidly toward a solution. Here is another "language" problem:

Exercise: Picture a large piece of paper, the thickness of this page. In your imagination, fold it once (now having two layers), fold it once more (now having four layers), and continue folding it over upon itself 50 times. How thick is the 50-times-folded paper?

It is true that it is impossible to fold any piece of paper, no matter how big or how thick, 50 times. But for the sake of the problem, imagine that you can. When you either have the answer or have given up, continue.

Your *first fold* would result in a stack 2 times the original thickness. Your *second* would give you a stack 2×2 times the original thickness. Your *third:* $2 \times 2 \times 2$ times the original thickness. Extending this, if you are somewhat of a mathematician, you should recognize that the answer to the problem is 2^{50} times the original thickness (2^{50} happens to be about 1,100,000,000,000,000). If the paper is originally the thickness of typing paper, the answer is some 50,000,000 miles or over half the distance from the earth to the sun.

If you tried to attack this particular problem with visual imagery (the clever way to handle the monk puzzle) you probably could not get an answer, since it is next to impossible to accurately visualize 50 folds. If you attacked it verbally, you probably also had trouble. If you are familiar with doubling problems, you knew that the answer was a surprisingly big number, but still could not place a value on it. The correct language in this problem was clearly mathematics.

Choosing Your Problem-Solving Language

Once again, how did you select the mental strategy you used to work on this problem? How did you decide to use visualization, mathematics, or whatever? If you were faked into visualization by our mention of the monk problem, you chose it consciously. If you are really getting the message of this book, you consciously thought about various ways of working the problem and then picked one. However, many of you probably once again *unconsciously* selected a strategy and then unconsciously switched from one strategy to the other. As we said before, most people follow this *habit* pattern in problem-solving. Without conscious thought, a direction will occur in the mind. This direction may or may not be the right one. If it is a wrong one, another may or may not appear.

It is possible to aid this strategy selection by consciously considering the various languages of thought you might use. For instance, you could have read the paper folding problem and then said to yourself, "Let's see, this guy has been trying to sell me visual thinking. Can I solve it visually? I'll try a few folds. [Task becomes difficult.] What else could I try? Verbalization? Probably not—since it is a physical problem asking for quantitative data. Hey, quantitative—how about mathematics?" At this point, you either solve it by inspection (you're a pro), write out equations and solve them (semi-pro) or ask someone you know who knows math (amateur).

Here is another puzzle. Before you try thinking of the answer, examine the problem and see what mental languages seem appropriate. Then attack the problem in the most appropriate language:

> **Exercise:** A man and a woman standing side by side begin walking. Each takes the first step with the right foot. The woman takes three steps for each two steps of the man. How many steps does the man take before their left feet simultaneously reach the ground?

This is a good problem to solve with visual thinking. A live experiment with another person, a drawing, or a musical rhythm analogy will all work well. A mathematical approach will work, although it is somewhat circuitous. Verbalization, once again, will not get you very far. What language did you pick? Did it work? Did you try alternate approaches? How did you know it was time to give up on one and try another? The answer is that their left feet never hit the ground simultaneously.

Choice of the proper problem-solving language is difficult not only because the choice is usually made unconsciously, but also because of the heavy emphasis on verbal thinking (with mathematical thinking a poor second) in our culture. The two problems you just worked were difficult because neither can be easily solved by the application of verbal thinking. Visualization, as expressed through the use of drawings, is almost essential in designing physical things well. One reason for this is that verbal thinking, when applied to the design of physical things, has the strange attribute of allowing one to think that he has an answer when, in fact, he does not. Verbal thinking among articulate persons is fraught with glib generalities. And in design it is not until one backs it up with the visual mode that he can see whether he is fooling himself or not.

One can also talk about the inflexible or inadequate use of problem-solving strategies as a type of awareness block. David Straus, founder of Interaction Associates, has for some time been concerned with the effective use of thinking strategies. Interaction Associates trains facilitators for problem-solving groups, offers educational programs, and conducts research in problem-solving. In one of their publications, *Summary of Basic Concepts*, they explain:

Each physical action or operation that we make to solve a problem can be seen in terms of a more general conceptual approach, useful in solving any problem. It is the rationale or purpose behind your actions: the "why" as opposed to the "what." This general, conceptual approach we call a "strategy." In our terms, the concept inherent in a strategy is independent of context. In other words, a strategy should be able to be used in almost all kinds of problems. We find that the strategic level is one of the most useful ways of talking about problem-solving.

Flexibility in Your Use of Strategies

Interaction Associates believes strongly in the effectiveness of becoming aware of specific thinking strategies. They have worked with problem-solving groups in educational, business, and political settings. One of its major techniques with all groups is to keep track of the strategy or strategies being used at any time during a problem-solving session and to suggest changes or additions if the problem-solving process appears to be bogging down or overlooking possible approaches to solutions. In their *Strategy Notebook* they list some 66 strategies, accompanying each with a description of the strategy, a list of its advantages and disadvantages, and a sample exercise. A list of the strategies contained in *Strategy Notebook* is shown below, along with a sample page.

Build up	Display	Simulate
Eliminate	Organize	Test
Work Forward	List	Play
Work Backward	Check	Manipulate
Associate	Diagram	Copy
Classify	Chart	Interpret
Generalize	Verbalize	Transform
Exemplify	Visualize	Translate
Compare	Memorize	Expand
Relate	Recall	Reduce
Commit	Record	Exaggerate
Defer	Retrieve	Understate
Leap In	Search	Adapt
Hold Back	Select	Substitute
Focus	Plan	Combine
Release	Predict	Separate
Force	Assume	Change
Relax	Question	Vary
Dream	Hypothesize	Cycle
Imagine	Guess	Repeat
Purge	Define	Systemize
Incubate	Symbolize	Randomize

Eliminate

POWERS The power of elimination lies in the possibility that you may be more sure of what you don't want than what you do want. This strategy requires beginning with more than you need or want in the solution and eliminating elements according to some determined criteria. There is an element of safety in this strategy because you have not overly extended yourself by deciding what you don't want in the solution.

LIMITATIONS This strategy assumes that within the realm of possibilities you are considering, there is a good solution. However, after you've finished eliminating, it's possible to end up with nothing. Another difficulty is that it is easy to infer that you want the opposite of what you have eliminated (i.e., you don't want rain, therefore you must want sunshine, leaving out the possibilities of snow, fog, hail, etc.). Thus elimination must be tempered by caution and good judgment.

EXERCISE — I GOT RELIGION Have each member of your group build upon the subject of religion. Each member should offer any ideas or associations he has with the subject, and the ideas should be recorded. Once the group is satisfied that they have exhausted their resources, each member of the group should take a piece of paper and a pencil and review the recorded list, eliminating whatever they don't want included in their personal religion or philosophy, and writing down on their lists anything that is left. Once everyone has finished, pin the sheets of paper to a display board so that the members of the group can share each other's ideas. This exercise has the advantage of allowing the participants to get personally involved in the subject matter through use of the strategy of elimination. The exercise can also be modified to encompass a variety of subjects. This may prove to be an effective introductory experience for a humanities or comparative religion class.

Most people have no trouble in understanding such problem-solving strategies, once definitions and examples are made available. In fact, most people have *unconsciously* used all of them at one time or another. However, since the mind is used to selecting strategies subconsciously, it takes awareness of these strategies and *conscious* choice or an outside facilitator to make the best use of them on a specific problem. The Introduction to *Process Notebook*, also by Interaction Associates, summarizes the situation as follows:

> Just as we use physical tools for physical tasks, we employ
> conceptual tools for conceptual tasks. To familiarize yourself
> with a tool, you may experiment with it, test it in different situations, and evaluate its usefulness. The same method can be
> applied to conceptual tools. Our ability as thinkers is dependent on our range and skill with our own tools.

It is obvious that a compromise has to be reached in the conscious selection of thinking modes and problem-solving strategies. One should not devote 95 percent of one's mental energy to the selection of strategies and thinking modes and reserve only 5 percent for the solving of the problem. Yet one should certainly spend some conscious effort thinking about strategies. First, by selecting strategies consciously one can often find approaches he would never have known about had he left the selection to his subconscious. Second, by becoming aware of various thinking strategies, what they can do, and how to use them, one can ensure that the mind has a larger selection when it utilizes its subconscious selection method. One can essentially become one's own "facilitator."

Importance of Correct Information

Lack of, or incorrect, information is a third conceptual block. As we discussed earlier, Arthur Koestler in "The Three Domains of Creativity" states: "The creative act consists in combining previously unrelated structures in such a way that you get more out of the emergent whole than you have put in." Other definitions of creativity also emphasize this "combining" aspect. Plainly we must have the components to combine (information). But let us look at what happens if we combine quantities which may include *incorrect* components.

If we combine two quantities, a and b, we have four possible results (a, b, ab, and ba). If a is incorrect, three of these results contain erroneous information. If both a and b are incorrect, all of them are contaminated. If we combine three quantities, a, b, and c, we have 15 possible results ($abc, acb, bac, bca, cab, cba, ab, ba, ac, ca, bc, cb, a, b, c$). If a is incorrect, 11 of these results contain erroneous information. If both a and b are incorrect, 14 of them are wrong. By playing with a little mathematics, we can come up with a general expression for this contamination tendency.

Let me first briefly refresh the memories of those who have studied math and perhaps enlighten those who have not. Let us assume that we have n elements. Then we see that there are a total of n possible arrangements (called combinations and permutations) which contain only one element. There are $n(n-1)$ arrangements containing two elements, $n(n-1)(n-2)$ arrangements containing three elements, and so on, until we reach the number of possible arrangements containing *all* n elements. (There are $n!$, read n factorial, which is equal to $n(n-1)(n-2)\dots(1)$, arrangements containing n elements.) Hence, the total number of arrangements (N) possible for n elements is the *sum* of the above terms. Or mathematically:

$$N = n + n(n-1) + n(n-1)(n-2) + \dots + n!$$

For example, if we want to know how many arrangements are possible when we have 4 elements (a, b, c, d), the solution is:

$$N_4 = 4 + 4(3) + 4(3)(2) + 4(3)(2)(1) = 64$$

Now to continue. We can use this expression not only to calculate the number of possible arrangements of n elements (N), but also to find the number of them that are affected by erroneous quantities. If *one* quantity of the n is wrong, the number of arrangements which do *not* contain the erroneous element is simply the number of arrangements which can be formed from the sum of all possible arrangements of $(n-1)$ elements. The number of arrangements containing false information is merely N minus this number of arrangements possible from $(n-1)$ elements. Similarly, the number of arrangements containing false information as a result of two erroneous quantities is N minus the number of arrangements possible from $(n-2)$ quantities. An example makes this clearer.

If $n = 4$, and 1 element is incorrect, then the number of arrangements in N which contain erroneous information can be calculated as follows:

Number of arrangements containing error $= N_4 - N_3$
$= [4 + 4(3) + 4(3)(2) + 4(3)(2)(1)] - [3 + 3(2) + 3(2)(1)]$
$= 64 - 15$
$= 49$ arrangements containing error

The following table contains a few numbers which indicate the advantages of correct information to the problem-solver. The first column represents the number of elements available to combine as Mr. Koestler would like us to. The second column indicates the number of arrangements available from the *n* elements. The third column gives the number of arrangements which contain erroneous information if one of the elements (*a*) contains error. The fourth column gives this number if two of the elements (*a* and *b*) contain error.

n	Possible arrangements	Erroneous if *a* is wrong	Erroneous if *a* and *b* are wrong
1	1	1	
2	4	3	4
3	15	11	14
4	64	49	60
5	325	261	310
6	1,956	1,631	1,892
7	13,699	11,743	13,374
8	109,600	95,901	107,644
9	986,409	876,809	972,710
10	9,864,100	8,877,691	9,754,500

These simple-minded numbers are not intended to be a model of conceptualization. I merely throw them in to demonstrate how rapidly combinations containing erroneous information build up as incorrect elements are introduced.

During the solution of a problem correct and adequate information is, of course, extremely important. An intellectual block which may prevent the problem-solver from acquiring well-balanced and pertinent information can be disastrous. Mechanical engineers with a block against electrical engineering or electrical engineers with a block against mechanical engineering may design strange things, such as mechanical television sets or complex electrical power transmission systems where simple mechanical ones would be cheaper and more reliable. People who consistently resist utilizing mathematics limit their problem-solving abilities by being blocked from useful quantitative data. Just as people who are blocked against considering aesthetic, emotional, and qualitative inputs in their decision-making also limit their problem-solving capabilities by refusing to acquire often useful information. Engineers who are uncomfortable with aesthetics can make outstandingly inhumane and ugly devices which may, as a side issue, not even sell well. Environmentalists who ignore the use of quantitative facts and statistics cannot be very productive in designing effective solutions to environmental problems.

There is, however, disagreement as to whether information is universally valuable at all phases of problem-solving. One school of thought maintains that one of the worst enemies of innovation is the large impact of existing solutions on conceptual thinking. This is the school that says: "It is difficult to think of alternate methods of felling small trees if one has spent a lot of time swinging an axe." I know one extremely inventive engineer who finds it very important to operate with a "clean" mind—he avoids learning anything about previous, related solutions to his problems. However, I know another equally productive engineer who spends a great deal of effort learning everything he can about every previous development that seems even slightly related to his problem (a "dirty" mind?). It is true that if one does not know about axes, his solution to felling small trees may be reinventing the axe. He is also denied the use of the axe as a source of additional concepts.

In my opinion, the optimal situation in problem-solving is to be able to use a clean-minded approach to a problem, even though one's mind is stuffed with information. I am, of course, biased by my own preferences. As I previously admitted, I grunt my way through problems instead of solving them in an effortless flash of insight. The more information I have about the problem and previous attempts to solve it, the better I do. However, it is sometimes necessary in the problem-solving process to hold this information at arm's length. Certainly, for instance, a massive amount of information is necessary when working with high technology, complex business situations, or interpersonal interactions. However, this abundant information can often prevent one from seeing very elegant solutions. Information makes one an expert, and William J.J. Gordon in *Synectics* says this about expertise: "The specialized semantics of established knowledge constitutes conventions which make reality abstract and secondhand. Learned conventions can be windowless fortresses which exclude viewing the world in new ways."

I believe that it is possible to be an expert and still view the world in new ways. One does not need someone who grew up alone on a desert island to invent a better can opener. One can use people who not only are quite knowledgeable about electrical, mechanical, physical, chemical, and whatever other phenomena, but who also have been closely associated with presently existing can openers. It is only necessary that these people be able to view the world in new ways in spite of all of their prior knowledge. If they can do this they should do better than someone from a desert island.

Expressive Blocks

Turning now to expressive blocks, let us begin by doing another simple exercise.

Exercise: This will require you to find (or make) a simple object whose shape cannot be described by a common name. It could be a block with a corner cut off and a groove along one face, a part from a machine, or any other object with a simple yet irregular three-dimensional shape. Do not use a pencil, a pair of scissors, a tonic water bottle, or other object which is so utilitarian and well known that its shape is familiar to everyone. Find several people, place the object you have chosen in a large paper bag, and have one of the people place his hand in the bag, without looking at the object. He is to describe the object to the other people, who are to draw it.

This exercise is surprisingly difficult. The lack of feedback in the communication loop is of course a contributor to this. Some feedback can be obtained by allowing those drawing the object to ask questions of the describer, although the exercise is most impressive when questions are not allowed. The exercise is also difficult because it is not easy to identify shapes by feel. However, the chief difficulty is probably that of describing a physical object verbally. If your volunteers are mathematically oriented and communicate in terms of x-y-z-coordinates or other geometrical surface description techniques, they will do better at this task. However, if the common verbal approach is used (e.g., "the bottom is a rectangular place with the corner cut off, and then there is a short side going up from the cut-off corner") the task is abysmally difficult. Another reason for the difficulty of the exercise is the rather low level of drawing talent developed in most people. Even if the shape could be perfectly described verbally, most people do not have the faculty to capture it on paper.

We usually do this exercise with a large group so that we can compare drawings after it is over (try it at a party). The presence of the audience adds some interesting emotional blocks. The person describing the object will do better if he or she spends some time feeling the object before describing it. However, it is difficult to spend this time in front of an impatient crowd. The person usually will plunge right into describing. The description will usually proceed at a rapid rate (even though the audience may be picking up no information of use) as the describer usually feels somewhat embarrassed standing in front of a group with his hand in a bag doing what to him may seem a trivial task. Since he will think he has a good idea of the shape of the object (he has his hand on it), he will find it difficult to believe that the audience does not. He may become impatient. He will undoubtedly demonstrate a form of incubation by thinking of a better way to have done his task after the exercise is over.

This exercise demonstrates both the use of *inadequate language skill* to express an idea and the *imprecision in our verbal expression*. It is an extremely common block which one finds often, for instance, in the engineering profession. Many students and engineers are not fond of drawing, partly because they may find it difficult and partly because in some fields drafting has somehow been given a lower status than, say, analysis. We find continual attempts, therefore, to communicate geometrical ideas verbally. Often the degree of difficulty induced by this expressive block is not even appreciated, since the describer knows exactly what he is trying to describe, and the describee often naturally assumes that he understands exactly what the other man is describing. Another problem that demonstrates this block of imprecise verbal expression (if you have access to a dozen people or so) is the following.

> **Exercise:** Give a person a drawing of a simple object (once again an abstract object so a name does not describe its shape). Ask him to look at it awhile and then describe it verbally to another person. The second person should then describe it verbally to a third person, and so on. This should be done in a manner so that the others in the group cannot overhear the descriptions. When the description of the object has been passed through ten people or so, have one last person draw the object. Comparison of the final drawing with the original drawing should prove fascinating.

Other examples of expressive blocks are easy to find: the frustration of trying to present concepts in a foreign language over which one has poor control is typical; the frustration of the writer who is an accomplished typist when his typewriter is broken and he must revert to longhand; the frustration of the executive whose Dictaphone is away for repairs or whose favorite stenographer is sick. These are all situations in which slowness of expression impedes the problem-solver.

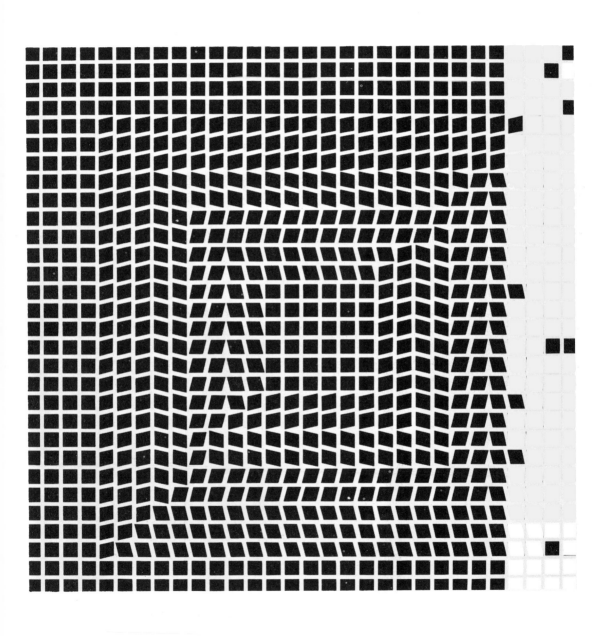

CHAPTER SIX

CONSCIOUS BLOCKBUSTING

THUS FAR IN OUR discussion we have been concerned with attempting to identify conceptual blocks. In this and the next two chapters, I will discuss some techniques of *overcoming* such blocks. This chapter will explore the handling of conceptual blocks by consciously overpowering them. The following chapter will discuss alternative thinking languages. The final chapter will be concerned with methods of becoming more relaxed, less critical, and more intellectually playful during problem-solving.

The process of consciously *identifying* conceptual blocks takes one quite a distance toward *overpowering* them. Still, there are specific methods of going further. Many of these blocks exist because of the achievement-oriented, competitive, and compulsive nature of Western man. However, this very combination of characteristics outfits him optimally for consciously overpowering such blocks. We think that people who are interested solely in good grades are often not as creative in school as they could be. However, if they are put in a course which is graded on creative output, they become much more creative. Their motivation and mental discipline are sufficient that they quickly figure out ways to become more creative and act accordingly. Let us talk about a few such methods which can be consciously applied to problem-solving.

A Questioning Attitude

One of the most important capabilities in a creative person is a questioning attitude. Everyone has a questioning attitude as a small child, because of the need to assimilate an incredible amount of information in a few years. The knowledge which one acquires between the ages of o and 6, for instance, enormously exceeds what has been consciously taught. A great amount of knowledge is gained through observation and questioning. Unfortunately, as we grow older many of us lose our questioning attitude. There are two principle reasons. The first is that we are discouraged from inquiry. After the child reaches a certain age, parents and others are often not as patient with questions (especially if they are busy and/or do not know the answer) which do not seem socially pertinent (Why can you see through glass? Why are leaves green?) and tend to discourage the questioner. Our educational institutions can barely convey the knowledge they are held responsible for (reading, writing, arithmetic, cultural lore). There is little time available for answering questions, so questions are effectively limited and discouraged. Many is the professor who begins his lecture with a plea for questions and then ends it with neither the time nor the encouraging attitude necessary to get them.

The second reason the child's "inquisitive" nature is socialized out of us (or at least diminished) has to do with "the great knowledge game." We learn as we grow older that it is good to be smart. Smartness is often associated with the amount of knowledge we possess. A question is an admission that we do not know or understand something. We therefore leave ourselves open to suspicion that we are not omniscient. Thus, we see the almost incredible ability of students to sit totally confused in a class in a university which costs thousands of dollars a year to attend and not ask questions. Thus, we find people at cocktail parties listening politely to conversations they do not understand, and people in highly technical fields accepting jargon they do not understand. One of my colleagues from my aerospace days used to delight in feeding nonsense jargon and erroneous arguments to people in other specialties. They would seldom question him in sufficient depth to find that he was faking. I have another friend who once successfully delivered a totally fraudulent hour-long lecture in aerospace medicine, of which he is totally ignorant, to an audience of university students. When his true credentials (none) were revealed to the students at the end of the lecture, they immediately voiced doubts that they had accumulated during the hour. They also registered extreme displeasure both toward the speaker and the instructor for violating their trust and wasting their time. However, during the talk itself, the competence and facts of the speaker were not questioned, probably because of the confidence with which he spoke and his extremely articulate lecturing style.

As I previously said, the questioning attitude is necessary in the broadest sense to motivate conceptualization. If one accepts the status quo unquestioningly, he will have no reason to innovate. He will not be able to see needs and problems, and problem-sensitivity is one of the more important qualities of the creative person. Once the problem is sensed, the questioning attitude must be used continually to ensure a creative solution. A creative person should have a healthy skepticism about existing answers, techniques, and approaches.

In a fascinating book called *The Universal Traveler. A Soft-Systems Guide to: Creativity, Problem-Solving, and the Process of Design*, the authors Don Koberg and Jim Bagnall discuss what they call "Constructive Discontent":

> Arrival at the age of 16 is usually all that is required for achieving half of this important attribute of creativity. It is unusual to find a "contented" young person; discontent goes with that time of life. To the young, everything needs improvement. . . . As we age, our discontent wanes; we learn from our society that "fault-finders" disturb the status quo of the normal, average "others." Squelch tactics are introduced. It becomes "good" not to "make waves" or "rock the boat" and to "let sleeping dogs lie" and "be seen but not heard." It is "good" to be invisible and enjoy your "autonomy." It is "bad" to be a problem-maker. And so everything is upside-down for creativity and its development. Thus, constructive attitudes are necessary for a dynamic condition; discontent is prerequisite to problem-solving. Combined, they define a primary quality of the creative problem-solver: a constantly developing Constructive Discontent.

This questioning attitude can be achieved by conscious effort. One merely needs to start questioning. An emotional block is involved here, since one is apparently laying his ignorance out in the open. However, it is a block that will rapidly disappear once one discovers the low degree of omniscience present in the human race. No one has all of the answers and the questioner, instead of appearing stupid, will often show his insight and reveal others to be not as bright as they thought. The most learned man can be overrun merely by continually applying the question "why?" or "how?" Pick a scientist, for instance, and ask him a "naive" question about something in his discipline. A few questions will drive him back through the basic knowledge which exists. Most of the questions you used to wonder about in your youth (What is beyond the farthest star? What is life? Why do people die?) are still unanswered.

In fact, the man who often is most admired at scholarly meetings is the penetrating questioner, who asks the apparently simple question which points out the flaws in a complex theorem or other structure of knowledge. Therefore, you have nothing to lose and a great deal to gain by questioning. The only thing you need to remember is that everyone is not as enlightened about knowledge as you (now) are, and some people will become unhappy if questioned to the degree that their omniscience becomes suspect. ("Why should man be creative?" "Because creativity allows self-actualization." "What good is self-actualization?" "It allows man to be happy." "What is happiness?" "Well-being." "What is well-being?" "Go to hell.")

If you still hesitate to ask questions, here are a few harmless and innocent questions. Ask them of anyone, and you will find that you are not as relatively ignorant as you thought.

1. Why do people sleep?
2. Do mirrors make letters appear backwards? If so—why do they not make them appear upside down?
3. A canary is standing on the bottom of a large sealed bottle that is placed on a scale. He takes off and flies around the inside of the bottle. What happens to the reading of the scale? What if he is a fish and the bottle is full of water?
4. What is licorice made out of? Why is it black?
5. Many cosmologists presently agree that the universe was created by a big "bang," or explosion, and that all of the stars are traveling outward from the original "bang." What preceded the "bang"?

Exercise: Questioning is especially important in problem-finding and problem-definition. You are going to use questioning in this manner. To play the game you need a cooperative person who is in a profession with which you are not very familiar. This exercise may take a reasonable amount of time, but if the person is a friend of yours or is interested in activities such as this, he should not object. Begin by asking him questions and ask them until you have a specific problem in his profession isolated and defined. Don't be satisfied with a vague, overly general, big-picture problem (medical care for the aged is inadequate). Try for a specific problem statement that is obviously soluble with a small amount of effort (for example, the sight of a novocaine needle scares people).

As you ask your questions, be aware of where your difficulties lie. Are certain types of questions (personal?) more difficult to ask than others? Can you observe the difficult period which results when you have used up your "social" questions and have to get down to work? What is your subject's response to different types of questions? Do you find it interesting to find out so rapidly about another profession (you should)? Were you able to go from a very general problem statement to a specific one? Did you work with several problem statements on the way to your final one?

Fluency and Flexibility of Thinking

Fluency and flexibility of thinking can also be attacked consciously. List-making is one of the simplest, most direct methods of increasing one's conceptual ability. People often compile lists as *memory* aids (shopping lists, "do" lists). However, lists are less frequently used as *thinking* aids. List-making is surprisingly powerful, as it utilizes the compulsive side of most of us in a way which makes us into extremely productive conceptualizers. It does not require (in fact would suffer from) change in behavior and flourishes in a competitive environment.

> Exercise (Part I): In order to give you a better feel for list-making, let me give you an exercise based on the "brick use" test attributed to J.P. Guilford. Imagine that you are a consultant for a brickyard which makes common red construction bricks and is in financial difficulties. The manager of the brickyard is interested in new uses for his products and has asked you to provide him with some. Spend a few minutes (three or four) thinking about the problem and then write down on a sheet of paper a new use for bricks.

Were you aware of what went on in your mind when you were thinking about the problem? You probably did some type of ad-hoc listing of alternatives. However, your conceptualization may have suffered from lack of focus, premature judgment (rejecting ideas which seem impractical), and labeling (choosing only the stereotyped usages).

> Exercise (Part II): Now take a blank piece of paper and spend four minutes listing *all* of the uses you can think of for bricks. Remember to aim for fluency and flexibility of thinking and not get hooked into premature judgment or labeling. Go.

You may have noticed (especially if you did this exercise with others) that people tend to be very intense when listing ideas, particularly when a time limit is involved. This is perhaps a remnant from our educational system and the general competitive nature of our society. However, whatever the cause, listing focuses one's conceptual energy in a rather efficient way and produces a written record of the output—both advantageous features. If the above exercise was successful, your "listing" effort should have gotten you much further conceptually than your original non-directed "spend a few minutes" effort. Were you fluent and flexible? As a calibration point in fluency, our design students average between 10 and 20 uses on this exercise. Some produce between 5 and 10, others between 10 and 20, and others between 20 and 30; a few produce under 5 or over 30 the first time through. The curve is roughly bell-shaped. *Fluency*, of course, is not enough in conceptualizing.

If your list were to consist of entries such as "build a wall, build a fireplace, build a patio floor, build a shoestore, build a hardware store, build a clothing store, build a grocery store," and so on, you could have been fluent, but of limited use to the brickyard owner who is probably already familiar with these uses. *Flexibility* of thought is also needed. You are flexible if your list included usages such as the storing of water, the warming of sheets on cold nights, the leveling of dirt, raw material for sculpture, playground blocks for children, and objects for a new track-and-field event (the brick-put). Such usages show an ability to see beyond the conventional role of bricks.

If you were doing this exercise with others, swap lists around and read them. Remember that some of the ideas should strike you as funny, if your flexibility is working well. If your list is lacking in flexibility, you may be suffering from the "premature labeling" block we discussed in Chapter Two. The usage of bricks is heavily stereotyped (construction material).

In Chapter Two we discussed the listing of attributes of something rather than labeling it as a method to escape the inhibiting effects of premature labeling. Let me say a bit more about premature labeling here. Once a label (professor, housewife, Black, chair, automobile, laxative) has been applied, people are much less likely to notice the actual qualities or attributes of that which is labeled. This is a block to conceptualization, which often requires the combining of the characteristics of things in new ways. For instance, if I am trying to think of what to do with a warehouseful of chairs, if I think of them only as chairs, I can probably only think of such usages as sitting on them, standing on them, or using them for hitting villains in grade-B movies. If I think of the *attributes* of the chairs (fabric, padding, wooden legs, screws, etc.) I can think of many more usages. (Maybe I should take the chairs apart and sell the seats to people who attend football games, make purses from the leather back-covering, sell the screws as surplus hardware, and sell the wood to home craftsmen.)

The listing of attributes is a powerful way to rapidly get more insight into the possible usefulness of an object, which in turn is an advantage in conceptualizing. Let us briefly examine a typical object, namely me. I am a professor. Most of you, never having met me, can conclude quite a bit about me from that statement. However, let me list a few more of my attributes. I am also a husband, a father, an acceptable mechanic, machinist, and carpenter, a poor tennis player, a better basketball player, and a piano player. I tend to be happier in rural environments than in cities. I like a great deal of contact with other people in my work, but prefer a light and relaxed social schedule. I have a bad knee, a messy office, a Timex electric wristwatch, and a 1909 brown shingle house. I am 6′ 4″, have brown eyes, and let my crew cut grow past my collar when I came to Stanford in 1966. Now, as I list these attributes, you should get a better feel for me as a person, and therefore be able to develop better "uses" for me.

Getting back to bricks, let us list the attributes of a brick. Some of them are:

    weight

    color

    rectangularity (sharp edges, flat faces)

    porosity

    strength

    roughness

    the capacity to store and conduct heat

    poor capacity to conduct electricity

    hardness

Think of more, if you can, and add to the list. How about economic considerations? Aesthetic aspects? I am sure that you can now see that by taking any attribute (weight), it becomes rather easy to list non-conventional uses for a brick (anchor, ballast, doorstop, counterweight, holding down tarpaulins or waste newspapers, as projectiles in wars, riots, neighborhood rumbles, etc.). It is often a help in conceptualization to consider attributes instead of commonly used labels. Let me now give you an opportunity to try attribute listing.

Exercise: This exercise is best done with a group of people. However, it can be done with a minimum of two—you and someone whom you do not know too well (immediate family members and roommates are out). Do the following:

1. Sit somewhere comfortable facing each other. If you are doing this with a larger group of people, ask them to pair off by selecting the person they know the least in the group and then sit down somewhere comfortable facing each other.

2. Each person should think of a single label which describes himself (doctor, artist, lawyer, jock) and tell it to the other person.

3. Attributes should then be traded verbally. Each person should tell his partner a personal attribute ("I have size 11 feet") and then his partner should reciprocate ("I cry easily").

Thinking Aids

The result of all this (other than some discomfort stemming from the fact that you are being forced to describe yourself in some detail to a stranger) will be a rapid increase in your understanding of the complexities and potentials of the other person. This exercise, incidentally, is one which we use often not only to demonstrate attribute listing, but also to rapidly introduce students to each other. A clever use of attribute listing is contained in *The Universal Traveler* which authors Koberg and Bagnall call "Morphological Forced Connections." They give the following rules for their "foolproof invention-finding scheme" along with an example showing how their scheme works. Here it is:

Morphological Forced Connections

1. List the attributes of the situation.
2. Below each attribute, place as many alternates as you can think of.
3. When completed, make many random runs through the alternates, picking up a different one from each column and assembling the combinations into entirely new forms of your original subject.

After all, inventions are merely new ways of combining old bits and pieces.

Example.

Subject: Improve a ball-point pen.

Attributes:

Cylindrical Plastic Separate Cap Steel Cartridge, etc.

Alternates:

Faceted	Metal	Attached Cap	No Cartridge
Square	Glass	No Cap	Permanent
Beaded	Wood	Retracts	Paper Cartridge
Sculptured	Paper	Cleaning Cap	Cartridge Made of Ink

Invention: A Cube Pen; one corner writes, leaving six faces for ads, calendars, photos, etc.

Another use of attribute listing, credited to Fritz Zwicky, is called morphological analysis. It is an automatic method of combining parameters into new combinations for the later review of the problem-solver. For instance, in an example done by John Arnold and taken from *Source Book for Creative Thinking* by Parnes and Harding, the problem is to provide a new concept in personal transportation. First of all, three parameters of importance are selected (more than three could be selected, but they could not easily be drawn on a piece of paper and put into this book). Alternate possibilities for the three chosen parameters (motive power source, type of passenger support, and the media in which the vehicle operates) are then listed on three orthogonal axes as shown on the next page.

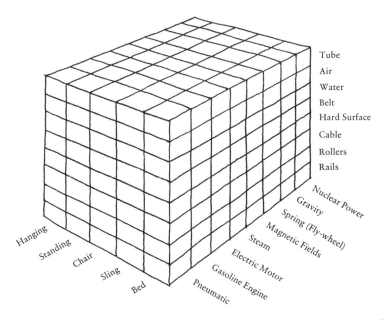

If we consider each box on the figure we have generated, we find that it represents a particular combination of our three parameters. For instance, one represents a steam-driven system that runs on rails and has passengers in chairs. This is not so interesting because it is a train and has already been thought of. So has the system which is driven by electricity and slings people from a cable (ski lift) and the gasoline engine powered one that seats people and travels on a hard surface. However, how about the pneumatic powered one in which people lie down and are transported through a tube, or the gravity powered one in which people stand and are transported down a belt? If one has access to a computer and can therefore consider large numbers of parameters, this technique can furnish enough combinations to keep the problem-solver well out of trouble as he sifts through them looking for something to spark an elegant solution to a problem. The creative "purist" would tend to scoff at this method as being too mechanistic. However, morphological analysis does, in fact, produce conceptual information.

Let me give you another example of the use of lists as thinking (rather than memory) aids. I am going to ask you to make a "bug list." People with a healthy fantasy life often play with the concept of inventing something the world needs and retiring on the proceeds. However, relatively few of them accomplish this. There are two factors which explain this lack of follow-through. The first is the difficulty in thinking of something specific that the world needs. The second is that it may require many years of apprehension, financial deprivation, and floundering family life before an invention can be made to pay off. The second factor is the more serious obstacle to this type of retirement. However, since it is not important unless the first hurdle can be cleared, and since we have no solutions here to the second aspect, let us pursue the first further.

In order to think of a potentially successful invention, it is necessary to establish a specific need. One way to establish or locate such a need is to interview people. For instance, you could go to the nearest hospital and start asking people on the staff what they needed. Another method is to play the role of a consumer group. Imagine you are a truck driver and see if you can think of something that you would need. A third, and perhaps simpler method, is to use yourself as the consumer. You must have needs which other people in the world share, and if you could identify such needs, you could invent something to satisfy them.

A problem which most people must cope with here is a tendency to generalize. If one of your needs is to eliminate air pollution or eliminate violence, you are setting yourself a tall task. (Better you have a need such as eliminating dog droppings from your front lawn.) The best way of starting on your retirement is probably to come up with a list of specific small-scale needs. A bug list is such a list. It contains as fluent and flexible and as specific and personal a list as possible of things that bug you.

> **Exercise:** Take a paper and pencil and construct such a list. Remember humor. If you run out of bugs before 10 minutes, you are either suffering from a perceptual or emotional block or have life unusually under control. If you cannot think of any bugs, I would like to meet you.

On the next page is a list of bugs from a few present-day Stanford student lists. After you are done see if your bugs are as flexible, specific, and personal as theirs. (You may also feel free to draw any conclusions you care to concerning students from this list on your own time.)

If properly done, your bug list should spark ideas in your mind for inventions. The list should ensure that specific areas of need are illuminated and that you have put in a reasonable amount of fluency and flexibility of thought. It should contain far-out bugs as well as common ones. For many of you, it may be the most specific thinking you have ever done about precisely what small details in life bother you.

After our students make such lists, we often ask them to turn them into inventions. Almost invariably, an interesting "invention" results. This requires first of all that the list be reduced to a few bugs of more than average potential. (Some preliminary thinking of solutions may occur here. Needs always seem to have more potential if a clever solution is available). Next we ask them to produce several concepts for the solution of each chosen bug. We then ask them to choose a concept and work it out in detail (including physical designs, where pertinent, and implementation plans). You may try this process if you would like. If you succeed and make a lot of money, send me some of it and I will use it for a charitable cause (my house payments).

Bug List

TV dinners
buying a car
relatives
paperless toilets
men's fashions
rotten oranges
hair curlers in bed
hypodermic needles
    for shots
sweet potatoes
cleaning the oven
no urinals in home
    bathrooms
bumper stickers that
    cannot be removed
broken shoe-laces
ID cards that don't
    do the job
pictures that don't
    hang straight
ice cubes that are
    cloudy
glary paper
swing-out garage doors
dripping faucets
doors that swell and
    stick in damp
    weather
newspaper ink that
    rubs off
bikes parked in wrong
    place
lousy books
blunt pencils
burnt out light bulbs
panty hose
thermodynamics
dirty acquariums
noisy clocks

plastic flowers
instant breakfast
buttons which must
    be sewn
hangnails
small, yapping dogs
waste of throw-away
    cans
soft ice cream
crooked cue sticks
prize shows on TV
static charges—car,
    blankets, etc.
ditches for pipe that
    are dug too large
bathtubs
cigarettes
balls which have to
    be pumped up
changing from reg.
    to sunglasses
reading road map
    while driving
wobbly tables and
    chairs
big bunches of keys
shoe heels that wear out
campers that you can't
    see around
corks that break off in
    wine bottles
soap dishes that you
    can't get the soap
    out of
vending machines that
    take your money
    with no return
buzzing of electric
    shavers

pushbutton water taps
Presto logs
one sock
stamps that don't stick
chairs that won't slide
    on the floor
banana slugs
trying to get change
    out of pockets
red tape
smelly exhausts
high tuition
writing letters
strip mining
dull knives
conversion of farm
    land to homes
chlorine in swimming
    pools
polishing shoes
broken spokes
stripped threads
cold tea
X-rated movies that
    shouldn't be X-rated
bras
mowing lawns
locating books in
    library
miniature poodles
parents' deciding a
    kid's career
solicitors—telephone
    and door-to-door
typewriter keys
    sticking
shock absorbers that
    don't work
shaving

Another type of list is the "check list." This is a list which one can apply to the thinking process to make sure that one has not been trapped by blocks. John Arnold, founder of the Design Division at Stanford and one of the pioneers in design education, used a check list first put forth by Alex Osborn in his book *Applied Imagination*. It is reproduced below.

Check List for New Ideas

Put to other uses?
New ways to use as is? Other uses if modified?

Adapt?
What else is like this? What other idea does this suggest? Does past offer a parallel? What could I copy? Whom could I emulate?

Modify?
New twist? Change meaning, color, motion, sound, odor, form, shape? Other changes?

Magnify?
What to add? More time? Greater frequency? Stronger? Higher? Longer? Thicker? Extra value? Plus ingredient? Duplicate? Multiply? Exaggerate?

Minify?
What to subtract? Smaller? Condensed? Miniature? Lower? Shorter? Lighter? Omit? Streamline? Split up? Understate?

Substitute?
Who else instead? What else instead? Other ingredient? Other material? Other process? Other power? Other place? Other approach? Other tone of voice?

Rearrange?
Interchange components? Other pattern? Other layout? Other sequence? Transpose cause and effect? Change pace? Change schedule?

Reverse?
Transpose positive and negative? How about opposites? Turn it backward? Turn it upside down? Reverse roles? Change shoes? Turn tables? Turn other cheek?

Combine?
How about a blend, an alloy, an assortment, an ensemble? Combine units? Combine purposes? Combine appeals? Combine ideas?

PROFESSOR BUTTS, TRAINING FOR THE OLYMIC GAMES, BROAD JUMPS INTO THE GRAND GANYON BY MISTAKE AND, BEFORE HE REACHES BOTTOM, HAS PLENTY OF TIME TO INVENT A NEAT LITTLE FIRE EXTINGUISHER.
PORTER A) SMELLS SMOKE COMING FROM ROOM AND IN THE EXCITEMENT STICKS HIS HEAD THROUGH WINDOW SCREEN TO INVESTIGATE. LITTLE BOY REMEMBERING CARNIVAL, THROWS BASEBALL B) WHICH BOUNCES OFF PORTER'S HEAD AND BREAKS GLASS IN AQUARIUM C), CAUSING WATER TO RUN INTO TROUGH D) AND REVOLVE PADDLE WHEEL E) WHICH WINDS ROPE F), PULLING KNIFE G) AND CUTTING CORD H). SHOE I) FALLS ON BABY'S FACE, BABY SHEDS COPIOUS TEARS. SPLASHING OF TEARS MAKES BULL FROG J) THINK OF BABBLING BROOK AND HE STARTS SWIMMING CAUSING FILE K) TO CUT CHAIN L) WHICH BREAKS AND ALLOWS TREES M) TO SNAP UPRIGHT AND PULL WET BLANKET N) OVER BURNING WASTE BASKET, THEREBY EXTINGUISHING FIRE.
IF THE FIRE DOESN'T HAPPEN TO BE IN THE WASTE BASKET, CALL OUT THE FIRE DEPARTMENT.

Professor Arnold had this check list put on a deck of cards, which he would ruffle through to see whether any of them would extend his thinking.

Koberg and Bagnall suggest in *The Universal Traveler* a list of what they call "manipulative" verbs—Osborn's original check list could be augmented by adding such words as:

Multiply	Distort	Fluff-up	Extrude
Divide	Rotate	By-pass	Repel
Eliminate	Flatten	Add	Protect
Subdue	Squeeze	Subtract	Segregate
Invert	Complement	Lighten	Integrate
Separate	Submerge	Repeat	Symbolize
Transpose	Freeze	Thicken	Abstract
Unify	Soften	Stretch	Dissect, etc.

Another type of check list is the one below, developed by George Polya of Stanford for use in solving single-answer mathematical problems. It first appeared in his book *How to Solve It*. This list not only exercises

questioning ability, but also your fluency, flexibility, and originality
through increased observation and association.

Understanding the Problem

What is the unknown? What are the data? What is the condition? Is it possible to satisfy the condition? Is the condition
sufficient to determine the unknown? Or is it insufficient? Or
redundant? Or contradictory? Draw a figure. Introduce suit-
able notation. Separate the various parts of the condition. Can
you write them down?

Devising a Plan

Have you seen it before? Or have you seen the same problem
in a slightly different form? Do you know a related problem?
Do you know a theorem that could be useful? Look at the unknown! Try to think of a familiar problem having the same or
a similar unknown.

Here is a problem related to yours and solved before. Could you use it? Could you use its results? Could you use its method? Should you introduce some auxiliary element in order to make its use possible? Could you restate the problem? Could you restate it still differently? Go back to definitions.

If you cannot solve the proposed problem try to solve first some related problem. Could you imagine a more accessible related problem? A more general problem? A more special problem? An analogous problem? Could you solve a part of the problem? Keep only a part of the condition, drop the other part; how far is the unknown then determined, how can it vary?

Could you derive something useful from the data? Could you think of other data appropriate to determine the unknown? Could you change the unknown or the data, or both, if necessary, so that the new unknown and the new data are nearer to each other? Did you use all the data? Did you use the whole condition? Have you taken into account all essential notions involved in the problem?

Carrying Out the Plan

Carrying out your plan of the solution, check each step. Can you see clearly that the step is correct? Can you prove that it is correct?

Examining the Solution Obtained

Can you check the result? Can you check the argument? Can you derive the result differently? Can you see it at a glance? Can you use the result of the method for some other problem?

List-making techniques can be used by anyone to assemble alternate concepts. They apply to the most rigid thinker as well as the most playful. They not only ensure good definition, but also that the ideas will last, since they are committed to paper. As we have already mentioned, ideas beget other ideas. If they are listed, they will lie around for days goading the idea-haver into other thoughts.

In a sense, such techniques as design notebooks, idea books, and problem journals are list-making techniques. A chronological record of a problem-solution is a list of all of the thoughts that have occurred during the solution of the problem. By its very existence, it causes the problem-solver to have more and increasingly imaginative concepts, especially if occasionally reviewed by others. We ask most of our students to keep design notebooks during their project work. These notebooks are complete chronological records of the thinking they have done and the information they have acquired. We collect them periodically for grading. We know that many of the students consider the notebooks to be an odious task and of questionable value and make most of their entries the night before we collect them. The impact this last minute "keeping up to date" has on their thinking is obvious. Groups that are apparently stuck on a problem will magically come up with new approaches the day that they hand in their notebooks. The intensive list-making they go through when padding up their notebook to meet our expectations is a powerful stimulus to conceptualization.

Other "conscious" blockbusters can be found in almost any "how to do it" book on creativity. Several of these are mentioned in the Reader's Guide at the end of the book. Most of them utilize some degree of list-making. Most of them include some gimmick to encourage playful thinking without the requirement of confronting playfulness head-on. Most of them work, although effort is required to utilize them in a real-istic problem-solving situation. The tendency of most teachers and authors (myself included) when trying to show the power of a technique is to include a sample problem which is a set-up for demon-strating it. Usually it is a simple problem which can be instantly solved if the technique is used and only with difficulty if it is not (e.g., visuali-zation—the monk puzzle). The game becomes more difficult when one leaves sample problems.

However, if one acquires sufficient practice with conscious block-busters, they can be applied to complex "real" problems quite success-fully. In fact, after sufficient usage, they will become second-nature. The specific listing of conceptual blocks is a conscious blockbusting tech-nique. If specific examples are furnished, it is seemingly easy to gain an appreciation for these blocks. However, it is harder to identify them in one's own thinking, both because they are blocks and because one's thinking is usually more complex than the examples. However, if you put a good deal of conscious effort into looking for them, you will learn to identify them. You will learn what types of blocks to expect in various situations, aggressively search them out, and gleefully violate them.

CHAPTER SEVEN

ALTERNATE THINKING LANGUAGES

IN CHAPTER FIVE we discussed the conceptual block resulting from the improper choice of a problem-solving "language." In this chapter, I would like to elaborate on this point. The well-armed problem-finder/solver is fluent in many mental languages and is able to use them interchangeably to record information, communicate with the unconscious, and consciously manipulate. Some of these modes are more "natural" to us than others. They are often even more powerful when used in combination with each other than when used alone.

In this chapter I will discuss some of these thinking modes or languages and put in a plug for some that I do not think receive their fair share of emphasis. To introduce this discussion, let me give you the following exercise:

> **Exercise:** Imagine that you just gave a ride to a hitchhiker who turned out to be an eccentric wealthy builder. As a token of his gratitude, he offers to build an addition onto your house according to your specifications, asking only that the total budget not exceed $6,000. Conceptualize the addition you would ask him to build for you. As you work on this problem try to observe what is going on in your mind (concerning the addition, not the probability of the situation occurring).

Once again, you should have become aware of the difficulty in observing your thinking process as it swings back and forth between the conscious and the unconscious. However, were you roughly aware of what "languages" you employed? Did you think verbally? Quantitatively? Pictorially? Did you imagine smells? Sounds? Tactile sensations? Muscle sensations? Did you tend to work mostly in one language?

If you are typical of most people, you will most easily recall the thinking you did that was in a verbal mode. Verbal thinking is the most prestigious (and perhaps most common) mental language in our culture.

Many psychologists and general semanticists feel that verbal languages are the basis of thinking. For instance, L.S. Vygotsky, in *Thought and Language*, says, "Thought is born through words." Edward Sapir in *Language* says that "language and our thought grooves are inextricably interwoven, are, in a sense, one and the same." Our educational systems reinforce this bias. As Rudolf Arnheim says in his essay "Visual Thinking," in *Education of Vision* (edited by G. Kepes): "In our schools, reading, writing, and arithmetic are practiced as skills that detach the child from sensory (as opposed to verbal or mathematical) experience. . . . Only in kindergarten and first grade is education based on the co-operation of all the essential powers of the mind. Thereafter this natural and sensible procedure is dismissed as an obstacle to training in the proper kind of abstraction." In our culture, we find much emphasis on reading speed and comprehension, on I.Q. tests which rely heavily on verbal ability, and on the use of verbal aptitude scores as an extremely important indicator of intelligence relating to academic and professional potential.

Being a verbal person, I would be one of the last to impugn the sagacity of those who would sanctify the word. It is certainly true that many problems can be well solved verbally. Such solutions can then be easily communicated through well-established verbal channels. However, as we saw in our monk puzzle and our paper-folding problem, there are also problems that can be solved verbally only with great difficulty. With this in mind consider the following problems.

> **Problem One:** Bob has three times as many pine cones as Dan. Between them they have 28 pine cones. How many does each have?

This problem can be worked verbally with the aid of logic, using a trial and error approach between the alternative possibilities. The solution to the problem is relatively simple. It can be solved algebraically as follows:

> let b stand for the number of Bob's pine cones
> let d stand for the number of Dan's pine cones

We know that the following relationships hold:

$$(1)\ b + d = 28$$
$$(2)\ b = 3d$$

Plugging in the second into the first and collecting terms, we find that $4d = 28$. Dan must therefore have 7 pine cones and Bob 21.

For any of you familiar with algebra, the mathematics involved here is trivial. Most of you, algebraic or not, are probably able to solve problems like this without too much distress. However, consider the next problem.

> **Problem Two:** Mary has three times as many pine cones as the pine cones owned by both Nora and Oscar. Dan has two times as many pine cones as Bob. Mary has one-and-a-half times as many pine cones as Dan. Oscar and Dan together have as many pine cones as the number Nora has plus twice the number Bob has. Bob, Dan, Mary, Nora, and Oscar have 28 pine cones between them. How many does each have.

I warn that if you are not familiar with algebra, this one will cause you a bit more distress. With sufficient trial and error work, it can be solved through logical verbal thought. However, the amount of work and bookkeeping is annoying, considering the unprofound nature of the problem. A mathematical approach is clearly advantageous. It can be solved algebraically as follows.

As we did before, let the number of Mary's pine cones be "m," the number of Nora's be "n," and the number of Oscar's "o." the relationships between these numbers (including Dan's "d" and Bob's "b") are:

$$(1)\ m = 3(n + o)$$
$$(2)\ d = 2b$$
$$(3)\ m = 3/2\ d$$
$$(4)\ o + d = n + 2b$$
$$(5)\ b + d + m + n + o = 28$$

As the mathematicians among you realize, these relationships give us enough equations to allow us to solve for all of the unknown numbers. A way (not the only way) to solve these is to first of all substitute the value for $n + o$ shown in relationship (1) into relationship (5), [i.e., $n + o = m/3$]. This gives:

$$b + d + 4/3\ m = 28$$

From relationship (2), we can see that $b = d/2$. Substituting this into the above, we get:

$$3/2\ d + 4/3\ m = 28$$

Relationship (3), however, tells us that $m = 3/2\ d$. Substituting this into our expression, we now get:

$$7/2\ d = 28$$
$$d = 8$$

Hence, Dan has 8 pine cones. Knowing this, we can then happily return to our original relationships and find that Bob has 4 pine cones [from relationship (2)], Mary has 12 [from (3)], and Nora and Oscar together have 4 [from relationship (5)]. Since relationship (4) now tells us that Oscar and Nora have the same number of pine cones, they have 2 each.

Some very simple mathematical language therefore leads us to an answer which requires a good bit of pain to reach verbally. Now you're ready for our third problem.

> **Problem Three:** Suppose that Nora, in a fit of pique, finds a ladder with which she plans to acquire as many pine cones as Mary. The ladder is 10 feet long and the tree trunk is vertical. Just as Nora reaches the top step of the ladder, it begins slipping. Suppose we wanted to know how fast Nora is dropping when the base of the ladder is 6 feet from the tree and is skidding along the ground at 5 feet per second, as shown below.

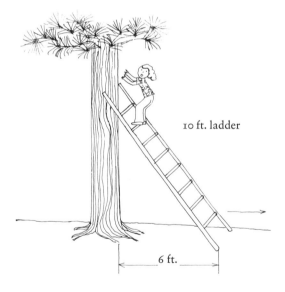

10 ft. ladder

6 ft.

How would you do on this one verbally? Probably not well at all because there is very little to guide you, and a trial and error approach is difficult. Once again, mathematically it is simple, requiring only a

trace of trigonometry and calculus. If you abstract the situation as follows:

and call the distance from the base of the tree to the base of the ladder
x and the distance from the ground to the top of the ladder y, you
can apply the theorem of Mr. Pythagoras to write the relationships between these two quantities and the ladder length as:

$$x^2 + y^2 = l^2$$

Substituting 6 feet for x and 10 feet for l, we find that y is 8 feet. Now
if we differentiate (a basic calculus operation) this relationship with respect to time, we get:

$$2x\dot{x} + 2y\dot{y} = 0$$

where the dotted quantities are velocities. Substituting 6 feet for x,
8 feet for y, and 5 feet per second for $\dot{x}$, we find that $\dot{y}$ (the quantity we
want) is 3¾ feet per second. Once again, simple in the mathematical
language—difficult in the verbal.

Clearly, if one attempts to predict the behavior of objects in space,
components of complicated machines or structures, or populations and
resources, one must include mathematics among one's thinking modes.
If one cooks from recipes, balances one's bank account, or uses the directions on one's lawn fertilizer, he must also use mathematics. If one
does not use mathematics as a thinking mode, he is handicapped in
working with problems which demand quantification.

Although mathematical aptitude and performance are highly re-
spected in certain circles in our society, verbal aptitude and performance
are more generally admired. In fact, in some circles, mathematical il-
literacy seems to be a desirable characteristic. Some people seem to feel
the cultural need to reject mathematics and boast about their ineptness
with quantitative matters. Some eschew mathematics as though it were
automatic and without soul, a misconception, of course, since pure
mathematicians are motivated and guided by a highly developed sense

of aesthetics. Still, mathematicians are heavily stereotyped in the U.S., and mathematical fluency is much less important than verbal glibness in the majority of high-reward positions in this country. For instance, were I to run for the office of President of the U.S. (assuming that this is a high-reward position) I would probably not challenge my opponent to a mathematical problem-solving contest on national TV. In fact, if anything, I would probably conceal my mathematical ability in order not to lose the votes of all those who rejected math as disagreeable in their childhood.

If more people would utilize mathematics in problem-solving (even at a low level of competence) the overall quality of solutions would benefit. Mathematical and verbal thinking together allow much more powerful attacks on problems than verbal thinking alone. I will not further elaborate on the usefulness of mathematical thinking, since it is generally accepted. I discussed verbal and mathematical thinking rather to demonstrate that two thinking "languages" make one a more potent and sophisticated problem-solver, and that some languages are in higher repute (and more frequently relied upon) than others.

I would now like to discuss some languages which we in the Design Division feel are extremely valuable in conceptualization, and are used even less frequently than mathematics. These are the languages of the senses: sight, sound, taste, smell, and touch.

Visual Thinking

A particularly important mode of thinking, which I have referred to several times before and which is presently receiving increased attention academically, is visual thinking. For an excellent treatment of this subject read Bob McKim's *Experiences in Visual Thinking* and Rudolf Arnheim's *Visual Thinking*. Visualization is an important thinking mode which is especially useful in solving problems where shapes, forms, or patterns are concerned. Arnheim explains: "Visual thinking is constantly used by everybody. It directs figures on a chess board and designs global politics on the geographical map. Two dexterous moving men steering a piano along a winding staircase think visually in an intricate sequence of lifting, shifting, and turning . . ." All of us are used to using visual imagery in some situations. For instance, visual imagery is extremely common in dreams. It is also common if someone asks us a question about the appearance of a person or a place. But it is also used in conceptualization, at times when one would not obviously expect its use.

In *The Act of Creation* Koestler quotes Friedrich Kekule, the famous chemist who discovered the structure of the benzene ring in a dream after having devoted a great deal of conscious thought to its enigmatic structure. Kekule describes the discovery:

> I turned my chair to the fire and dozed. Again the atoms were gamboling before my eyes. This time the smaller groups kept modestly in the background. My mental eye, rendered more acute by repeated visions of this kind, could now distinguish larger structures, of manifold conformation; long rows, some-times more closely fitted together; all twining and twisting in snakelike motion. But look! What was that? One of the snakes had seized hold of its own tail, and the form whirled mock-ingly before my eyes. As if by a flash of lightning, I awoke.

The result of the dream was Kekule's brilliant insight that organic com-pounds such as benzene were *closed rings* rather than open structures.

In *Experiences in Visual Thinking* Bob McKim writes of three kinds of visual imagery that are necessary in effective visual thinking. The first, *perceptual imagery*, is sensory experience of the physical world; it is what one sees and records in his brain. The second is *mental imagery*, which is constructed in the mind and utilizes information recorded from perceptual imagery. The third type is *graphic imagery*. This is imagery which is sketched, doodled, drawn, or otherwise put down in a written communicable form, either to aid in one's own process of thinking or to aid in communication with others.

Let us first of all briefly consider perceptual imagery, or seeing. By asking you to draw a telephone dial in Chapter Two, I hope I convinced you that you do not record everything you look at, at least at an acces-sible level (under hypnosis, you might be enabled to draw the dial prop-erly). People see poorly for several reasons. As previously mentioned, one reason is an oversaturation of input. Another is lack of motivation. People tend to see better those things which are more important to them, more unusual, or of an easily-recorded visual character.

You can learn to see better through conscious effort, especially if you are convinced that seeing better is important to you. One way of rapidly developing your *seeing* ability is to engage in activities where you must reproduce things you have seen.

> **Exercise:** You can exercise your seeing ability by looking at things and then drawing them. Such an activity requires not only seeing but imagining and drawing, which will be dis-cussed later. Try this procedure with objects around you, or better yet, objects in your profession which you think it would be helpful to know more about.

A drawing course can improve your seeing ability. If you have to draw trees, you will really start seeing them. I took an art course once in which the teacher took delight in asking us to make quick sketches of friends, family, pets, home, and neighborhood. I found this extremely interesting because I looked at my immediate environment at least two orders of magnitude more closely. One of my colleagues took a photography course in which the instructor taught the students to photograph scenery by taking a jar of beans and the students into a field, throwing a bean into the field for each member of the class, and then telling each student to stand on his bean and spend the day shooting scenic pictures. Such exercises *make* one see. You can take pictures of the Grand Canyon or other scenic wonders without putting a great deal of effort into detailed seeing. However, taking a beautiful picture while standing on your bean in a field requires that you truly use your powers of visual perception.

Now let us talk about the second type of visualization: mental imagery. These mental images are probably the most important for the conceptualizer. According to McKim, there are two aspects of visual imagery which are important. The first he calls clarity (how sharp and filled with detail are the images?). The second he calls control (how well can you manipulate them?). Here is an exercise to let you evaluate your visual "imaging" capability.

> **Exercise:** *Clarity of Mental Images.* Imagine the following. After each mark a clear (c), vague (v), or nothing (n) in accordance with how clear (sharp and detailed) the image appears in your mind.
>
> 1. The face of a friend
> 2. Your kitchen
> 3. The grille on the front of your car
> 4. A camellia blossom
> 5. A fiddler crab
> 6. A Boeing 747
> 7. A running cow
> 8. The earth from orbit
> 9. Your first car
> 10. Richard Nixon

The clarity of one's mental images depends upon several factors. First of all, in this type of exercise, it depends on *seeing*. If you have never seen a fiddler crab or a running cow, your mental images were probably not too sharp. It also depends on one's seeing *ability*. And this in turn, as we have mentioned, depends on motivation (your camellia was probably clearer if you are a camellia freak), the visual character of the object (Richard Nixon was probably fairly clear because he has been characterized so often in the news and in political cartoons), timing (your first car may have grown dim by now), and saturation (your car grille?). Finally, it depends upon the image-reproduction mechanism of your brain. There is certainly individual variation in the ability to visually imagine which goes beyond the variability mentioned above. If you ask a roomful of people to visualize a brick or an apple, and then ask individual members of the room questions about their image, you will get a range of answers, the clarity of which extend from images vivid in color, detail, texture, background, and shadows, to no particular image at all.

> **Exercise:** For your own information try visualizing a series of objects and see if you can determine a pattern in your own imaging ability. Are you better at visualizing people than objects? Or worse? Are you better at two-dimensional objects than three-dimensional? Are you better at small things than large things? Where do you see your image? Is it out in front of your eyes or back in your skull somewhere?

Visual imaging ability is complex, since it depends not only upon one's ability to form images, but also upon the supply of pertinent imagery which is stored in the mind. However, it seems safe to say that one can improve one's visual imaging capability by devoting effort to it and making it a higher priority item in problem-solving. Visual images can be consciously enhanced. When I was a student of John Arnold at Stanford, he was constantly hitting me with "visualize an apple" type problems. As a result, I became so conditioned that when asked to visualize something I still concentrate all of the information and energy I can on the task. Now let us look at your ability to *control* (manipulate) visual imagery.

> **Exercise:** Imagine the following:
>   1. A pot of water coming to a boil and boiling over
>   2. Your Boeing 747 being towed from the terminal, taxiing to the runway, waiting for a couple of other planes, and then taking off
>   3. Your running cow changing slowly into a galloping racehorse
>   4. An old person you know well changing back into a teenager
>   5. A speeding car colliding with a giant feather pillow
>   6. The image in (5)—in reverse

Are you better at manipulating images you have actually seen or in creating new ones? Can you modify images in a fantastic (non-real) way? Take some time, and see whether you can extend your understanding of your ability to control your visual imagery. Try manipulating various types of images, inventing images in your mind, etc. Many people feel that the ability to control visual images can be developed through practice. Bob McKim in *Experiences in Visual Thinking* discusses what he calls "directed fantasy" as a way of strengthening imagination. In "directed fantasy" the participant is asked to fantasize in a numer of directions which take him through a wider range of imaginative activities. He is forced to "exercise" his imaginative abilities and confront imaginative blocks which he would ordinarily avoid. By finding that he is able to wander freely through these areas and allow his imagination to range widely without catastrophic results, he becomes encouraged to feel more familiar with the use of visual imagery in conceptualization.

Now let us discuss the third type of visualization—graphic imagery. In order to take full advantage of visual thinking ability, *drawing* is necessary. Drawing allows the recording, storage, manipulation, and communication of images to augment the pictures one can generate in his imagination. In the Design Division, we find it useful to divide drawing into two categories: that which is done to communicate with others, and that which is done to communicate with oneself. The following drawing is a type used generally for the purpose of communicating with others. It was drawn by architect Walter Thomason of San Francisco.

Drawings such as these idea sketches are generally used in communicating with oneself. They were drawn by a Stanford engineering graduate student, Peter Dreissigacker. (Yours need not be as artistic.)

The first type of drawing (communicative) receives a good bit of attention educationally, and one can learn to make such drawings through formal courses of instruction. The second type (thinking sketches) receives far less emphasis, yet it is an important adjunct to visual thinking. Given a large pad of paper and a pencil, most people will make sketches as they work on sample problem exercises. Strangely enough, the same people often will not go to the trouble of summoning their drawing materials on their own in a problem-solving situation.

As I have previously mentioned, we work with an extremely verbal group of students at Stanford. A great deal of effort has been put into their verbal (and mathematical) abilities during their formal education, but little into their visual ability. When they come to Stanford many are, in Bob McKim's frustrated terminology, "visual illiterates." They often are not used to drawing, nor to using visual imagery as a thinking mode. Although their drawing is generally not good, it is usually good enough (especially with a few helpful hints) to use as a thinking aid. Nonetheless, they are usually extremely reluctant to draw because their drawings compare so badly with drawings made by professionals (intended for communication with others). We try to encourage crude but informative drawings for the student's own purposes. We also try to encourage improving one's drawing skills, since we find that good drawing skill is a powerful conceptual aid. Try the following exercise and see whether your drawing skills (no matter how marginal) help you in conceptualizing.

> Exercise: Buy a cheap notebook of a convenient size (small enough to accompany you, but as big as possible otherwise) and provide yourself with the most satisfying line-maker you can find. (A good one is a Pentel-type pen, which looks like a ballpoint pen but has a tapered fiber tip that makes an instant dark and smooth line.) Make drawings for yourself in this notebook for the next week or so while you are conceptualizing and otherwise involved in solving problems. Your drawings may be doodles, block diagrams, schematics, squiggles, sketches, or what have you. Try to see which of these drawings (if any) help in problem-solving and which do not. Are they of more use in particular portions (e.g., at the beginning) of the problem-solving process? Does a lack of drawing-skill minimize their effect? Do you use your notebook to refer to your previous work? Does the size of your notebook inhibit you? (If so change to newsprint or butcher paper on the wall or a table and to larger felt pens or to color, and try again.)

By emphasizing drawing as a thinking technique, I do not mean to belittle its power as a communication device. I have had many experiences in which people who are able to draw well have been able to influence others in a problem-solving situation, for better or worse. This is especially prevalent in design situations where no precedent exists. I was recently supervising a student group engaged in the design of a new type of underwater vehicle. One of the students was excellent at making quick renderings. Each time he would put forth a concept it would seem so real in its rendered form that the group would gleefully adopt it. Then, when he produced another concept the next day, the group would be in temporary consternation until they adopted the new one. I have seen the same thing happen many times in the design of spacecraft, where little visual precedent exists. A well-drawn concept has amazing power. Drawings, of course, also have amazing ability to convey precise information, even if crudely done. One of my oldest and best friends, for instance, is a farmer. When I visit him I often accompany him on his rounds. Since I am a helpful sort, I try to aid him in his various projects, which often consist of moving large inert objects. Such tasks should be straightforward to someone like me, who is, after all, an engineering professor. However, he gives directions verbally, with the result that I am always bewildered by a version of the situation we encountered in the block-in-the-bag exercise in Chapter Four. (I am on a long-term project of getting him to draw crude pictures for his people and for me, so I will not stupidly put things in the wrong place.)

> **Exercise:** Use your drawing skills, no matter how marginal, to aid you in giving directions to people. Carry a small pad and pencil to do this if necessary. You are probably familiar with drawing crude maps to show people how to get to your house. But have you ever drawn your children a map of where to pile the leaves they are raking up, your husband a map of how to put things away in the house, or your wife a map of how to carve a roast (sorry for any role typing)?

Let us now leave visual imagery, an extremely important tool in conceptualization. If you have the time and inclination to attempt to develop your visual thinking ability, the Reader's Guide will give you places to start. At least become aware of your abilities and limitations with visual imagery and attempt to use visualization in your thinking process whenever appropriate. It is one of the most basic of all thinking modes and one which is *invaluable* in problem-solving.

Other Sensory Languages

We will now go on to other sensory languages which are essential in conceptualization and are used even less frequently in general problem-solving than visual thinking. Just as visual imagery corresponds to the sense of sight, other types of sensory imagery also result from their corresponding senses.

Here are some exercises for you to test how good you are at different types of sensory imagery. Once again, rate them clear (c), vague (v), or nothing (n).

Exercise: Imagine:
   The laugh of a friend
   The sound of thunder
   The sound of a horse walking on a road
   The sound of a racing car
   The feel of wet grass
   The feel of your wife's/husband's/girlfriend's/
       boyfriend's/pet's hair
   The feel of diving into a cold swimming pool
   The feel of a runny nose
   The smell of bread toasting
   The smell of fish
   The smell of gasoline
   The smell of leaves burning
   The taste of a pineapple
   The taste of Tabasco sauce
   The taste of toothpaste
   The muscular sensation of pulling on a rope
   The muscular sensation of throwing a rock
   The muscular sensation of running
   The muscular sensation of squatting
   The sensation of being uncomfortably cold
   The sensation of having eaten too much
   The sensation of extreme happiness
   The sensation of a long attack of hiccups

Now try the following for control of separate sensory images:
   The sensation of being uncomfortably cold changing to one
       of being uncomfortably hot
   The laugh of a friend changing into the sound of thunder
   The feel of wet grass changing into the feel of your wife's/
       husband's/girlfriend's/boyfriend's/pet's hair
   The smell of fish changing into the smell of gasoline
   The muscular sensation of pulling on a rope changing into
       the muscular sensation of rowing a boat

Such exercises have a function equivalent to the earlier exercises on visual imagery. They may help you develop your sensory imagery ability, if used extensively. In any case, they at least let you learn more about your ability to image in various sensory languages.

Sight tends to be the predominant sense from a physiological standpoint. However, just as verbal thinking should not be allowed to elbow visual thinking out of the way, neither should the visual mode be allowed to overpower other sensory modes. Smell, sound, taste, and touch are extremely important to problem-solvers for three reasons:

1. Since they are low on the thinking "prestige" list in our culture they can lead you to innovative and overlooked solutions. (Tarzan had a well-developed sense of smell, but I am sure that no one would *expect* the same from a Nobel Prize winner.)
2. They are necessary for the solution of problems in which smell, sound, taste, and touch are involved (the design of a new hors d'oeuvre).
3. They augment visual imagery and each other to vastly increase the clarity of one's total imagery (more about this later).

Let us briefly discuss the first reason listed above. We often give our students problems having to do with developing devices to help blind people. We do this both because it proves highly motivating and requires ingenuity, and because it makes them think about various types of sensory inputs. Most of them attack the problem initially by imagining that they are blind. This is difficult to do, because sight is such an overwhelming input to most people that they find it hard to take the role of a blind person using their imagination alone. They especially find it hard if they generally think only verbally or mathematically.

After letting them work on the problem a while, we blindfold the students for an hour or two and let them wander about the world. This gives them, all at once, a chance to accept input from their other senses. They are then much more likely to use this very important data (to a blind person) to solve their problems. This simulation of blindness has limited accuracy, because when one is blindfolded for an hour or two his main problems have to do with walking, whereas blind people have long since overcome this. Still, the simulation is effective in bringing the awareness of messages from the other senses to people.

> **Exercise:** Try this experience yourself. Find someone to keep you out of trouble (not to physically guide you, just to keep you off the freeway, out of open manholes, poison oak, etc.), blindfold yourself, and walk around for an hour or so. You will be amazed at the sensory data you accumulate.

The second reason for using all the senses, "They are necessary for the solution of problems in which smell, sound, taste, and touch are involved," should be obvious. Just as an architect is better off with a good ability to image spaces and forms, so a cook is better off being able to image taste and smell.

The third point, "They augment visual imagery and each other," is more subtle. I am sure that most of you are aware that the senses augment each other. Food is a combination of taste, smell, and sight. Vichyssoise is as unsuccessful when one has a cold as an omelette is if it is dyed blue. An electrical storm needs sound as well as sight to be really dramatic. Sexual excitement benefits from feel, smell, and taste as well as sight and sound. Similarly, mental images need the full dimensionality of all the senses to be most effective.

In order to demonstrate this, I would like to give you another exercise. However, before you begin, I would like you to think of an apple. Got it? Now ask yourself enough questions about this apple that you can establish the clarity of your image.

I am now going to give you the transcription of a tape which Bob McKim and Bill Verplank use in a Stanford class in Visual Thinking. The tape is concerned with *clarity* and *control* of combined sensory imagery. It is played to small groups of students in an isolated and comfortable environment. They are typically sprawled comfortably on a soft, carpeted floor with no distractions present. They have been prepared for the tape by a talk explaining the serious purpose of the exercise and several weeks of class stressing the importance of sensory imagery.

Exercise:
 1. Find a sympathetic narrator and preferably a few other people who are interested in this subject.
 2. Obtain an outstanding apple for each person.
 3. Relax in a comfortable spot with the others.
 4. Have the narrator read the following to you. He should read slowly, seriously, and soothingly, giving you plenty of time to fully establish the images before he goes on. You can help by giving a prearranged signal (a lifted finger?) when you have the image fully developed, at which point he can go on to the next statement.

"First close your eyes and relax / Direct your attention inward / Now imagine yourself in a familiar setting in which you would enjoy eating an apple / Relaxedly attend the sensory mood and detail of this place / Now, imagine that in your hand you have a delicious, crisp apple / Feel the apple's coolness, / its weight, / its firmness, / its round volume, / its waxy smoothness / Explore its stem / Visually examine details, / see bruises, / the way sunlight sparkles on the facets of the apple's form, / the way the skin reflects a pattern of streaks and dots, many colors, not just one / Attend this image till your mouth waters / Now bite the apple / Hear its juicy snap, / savor its texture, / its flavor, / Smell the apple's sweet fragrance / With a knife, slice the apple to see what's inside / As you continue to explore the apple in detail, return occasionally to the larger context, / see your hand, / feel the soft breeze, / be aware of the three dimensionality of form and space.

"How was your apple this time? Probably a lot better. But your apple is probably still not as vivid as possible, simply because you don't really know what an apple is like. We've all eaten plenty of apples, but how often do we really pay attention. We are most often doing something else while eating, talking, reading, thinking, but never attending to every sensory detail. We're going to give each of you an apple now—a real apple this time—and you can eat it. We're going to ask that no one talk. All of your attention should be on the apple and on your sensations. Before you eat your apple, take a minute to examine it. Look at its shape, its volume, its color, its markings. Feel its temperature, its texture, its firmness, its mass. When your really know it, take a bite from it. Listen, smell, taste, feel, attend every sensory detail. Take your time.

"The apple that you have just eaten is now being assimilated by your digestive system. The apple is becoming you. Imagine that you are the apple that you have just eaten. Imagine that you are an apple on an apple tree. Take a deep breath. Let it out, and as you let it out, relax all tensions. Quiet all distracting thinking. Direct all of your attention, in a very relaxed way, to the pleasurable thought of being an apple on a real apple tree in a beautiful apple orchard way out in the country. You can feel the warm sun on your skin. You can feel a soft breeze. The sky is clear blue. The sun feels good as it radiates into your apple body. You can hear the leaves of your tree rustling in the breeze. You can smell the fragrance of the ripening apple orchard. It feels good to be part of nature. Now imagine that you are regressing in time. You are an apple that is going backward in time, becoming smaller, smaller, greener, tarter, smaller yet, you are evolving in reverse into an apple blossom. You are an apple blossom together with many other apple blossoms on your apple tree. You can smell the lush fragrance of apple blossoms. You can feel the warm sun on your delicate petals. You can hear the honey bees buzzing as they go about pollenating the orchard. In the distance you can hear a farmer's dog barking. You can taste your own sweet nectar. You can feel that you are an integral part of an incredibly complex natural process involving sun, earth, air, bees, the seasons. It feels good. Now you are becoming aware that you are more than a single apple blossom. You are an apple tree. Allow your imagination to move into the branch that supports the blossom. You can feel the sap that brings energy to the tree's leaves and blossoms. You can feel the sap moving through you. Follow this flow of energy down into the trunk of the apple tree. Feel the strength of the trunk in your own body. You must be strong to support branches loaded with ripe apples, and to resist the force of heavy wind. Feel the rough texture of your bark, the hardness of your wood. Now direct your attention down the trunk and into the roots of your apple tree. Reach out into the dark, damp soil. See the darkness. Smell the fragrance of the fertile soil. See the fat worms and the other subterranean creatures that work the earth. Feel the cool wetness and texture of the moist dirt and rocks, as your roots reach out for life-giving water and nutrients. Now leave the tree. Become the water itself in the damp orchard field. Feel yourself feeding the grasses and the wild flowers. You are part of a larger concept. You are essential to life. You are part of the much larger unity of nature. As water saturated in the orchard field, experience the sun's heat drawing you upward. Feel the sun evaporating your body, transforming your liquid nature into vaporous water. Feel your molecules rising upward into the blue sky toward the blazing sun. You and the others are now forming into a soft cloud. Down below you can see the earth, the tiny patch of the apple orchard, you are floating in the blue sky effortlessly. Quiet, billowy, incredibly free. In the distance a hawk is soaring. You are part of the creative cycles of nature. Now the sky is darkening, becoming cooler, you can feel the wind swirling and moving through your cloud. You are condensing with other molecules into droplets of rain. Falling downward, through the cold gray sky, downward, downward. You splash the leaves of a green apple tree and fall down to the ground, to the soil, to the roots, to the strong trunk, to the sap that feeds the branches, the leaves, the blossoms, the apple. You are the apple on the tree, in the orchard, on a rainy day. You can hear the rain splattering on the leaves, feel the cold stormy wind swaying the tree's branches, smell the rich odor of damp earth. Your apple, created by this marvelous interwoven working of nature, is inside you becoming you. And you, in turn, are a unique part of this creative unity. As you return now to your aliveness, here, and now, you feel good to be part of a unity which is inherently and eternally creative."

The students in the class do not use this tape until they have had quite a bit of experience in conceptualization, visualization, and imaging exercises of various sorts. However, we find that most people without

Portrait of Mʀ GOLIGHTLY,
experimenting on Mess. Quick & Speed's new patent high pressure,
STEAM RIDING ROCKET.

Pub by C. Tilt, Fleet St

this background are still able to build a crunchy luscious apple image in the first portion of the tape and enjoy their real apple with heightened sensory awareness. We find that people have more difficulty with the "control" portion of the tape and find it less relevant than the students do. However, it is useful as another indication of your ability to control imagery. You may now get a real apple from the refrigerator (if you haven't already) and eat it as you expand into the next chapter, which has to do with freeing the subconscious.

Conceptual Blockbusting • 111

CHAPTER EIGHT

UNCONSCIOUS BLOCKBUSTING

IN CHAPTER FOUR, we discussed the critical role played by the unconscious mind and its inhibition by the ego and superego. Chapter Six dealt with techniques by which one can consciously force his way through conceptual blocks. Through the use of various forms of listing and by consciously questioning and striving for fluency and flexibility of thought, it is possible to improve considerably one's conceptual performance. These techniques work by utilizing the intellectual problem-solving capability of the conscious mind. In this final chapter, we will be concerned with decreasing the inhibiting effect of the ego and superego on the unconscious mind.

One of the most powerful techniques of enhancing one's conceptual ability is the postponement of judgment mentioned in Chapter Four. The ego and superego suppress ideas by judging them to be somehow out of order as they try to work their way up to the conscious level. If this judging can be put aside for a while, many more ideas will live until they can be "seen." The dangers of premature judgment are alluded to in the following statement by Schiller (taken from a personal letter to a friend and contained in *The Basic Writings of Sigmund Freud*, edited by A. A. Brill).

> The reason for your complaint [about not being creative] lies,
> it seems to me, in the constraint which your intellect imposes

upon your imagination. Here I will make an observation, and illustrate it by an allegory. Apparently, it is not good—and indeed it hinders the creative work of the mind—if the intellect examines too closely the ideas already pouring in, as it were, at the gates. Regarded in isolation, an idea may be quite insignificant, and venturesome in the extreme, but it may acquire importance from an idea which follows it; perhaps, in a certain collocation with other ideas, which may seem equally absurd, it may be capable of furnishing a very serviceable link. The intellect cannot judge all those ideas unless it can retain them until it has considered them in connection with these other ideas. In the case of a creative mind, it seems to me, the intellect has withdrawn its watchers from the gates, and the ideas rush in pell-mell, and only then does it review and inspect the multitude. You worthy critics, or whatever you may call yourselves, are ashamed or afraid of the momentary and passing madness which is found in all real creators, the longer or shorter duration of which distinguishes the thinking artist from the dreamer. Hence your complaints of unfruitfulness, for you reject too soon and discriminate too severely.

Delaying judgment does not come easily to most people, since we are taught to be severe critics of anything impractical, unrealistic, flippant, flawed, or socially frowned upon. Often we do not want to admit, even to ourselves, the existence of such thoughts in our mind. We certainly do not want to admit to others that we might think of roofing a building with feathers, of reducing air pollution by substituting sedan chairs for automobiles, or perhaps even of legalizing heroin to reduce crime. However, our minds should be able to conjure up these and much wilder ideas if we are to be truly creative thinkers. How, then, do we delay judgment? As in Chapter Six we can begin with consciously applied techniques. Often if we can consciously make our ego relax a little, the success of the idea generation which follows may cause it to relax even further. We begin a game which is to some extent self-perpetuating. The easiest way to begin this game is to formally (by agreement with oneself or with others) establish a judgment-suspension session. Individually I may say to myself, "All right, I need some fresh ideas on this problem I am working on and I have a little time to spend, so I will suspend judgment and see what ideas I can think of. It doesn't matter if my thoughts are weird at times, since no one can see what I am up to." I am then free to conceptualize without judging the practicality of the ideas, since I am not imperiling my ego. After all, I officially announced to myself that I would undergo this activity and therefore it is not typical of my usual mental deportment.

Brainstorming

Suspending judgment in groups can be even more effective than suspending it individually, since a spirit of enthusiasm can develop in the group and ideas may spark ideas in others. I am sure you have heard of brainstorming, a group problem-solving technique given its name by Alex Osborn, the founder of the advertising firm of Batten, Barten, Durstine, and Osborn. Brainstorming groups usually consist of from five to ten people who work on a specific problem. Four main rules govern their behavior, according to Osborn.

The first rule is that no evaluation of any kind is permitted. Osborn's explanation is that a judgmental attitude will cause the people in the group to be more concerned with defending ideas than with generating them. His second rule is that all participants should be encouraged to think of the wildest ideas possible. His thinking here is that it is easier to tame down than to think up, and by encouraging wild ideas, internal judgment in the minds of the individual participants can be decreased. Thirdly, Osborn encourages quantity of ideas, both because quantity also helps to rule our internal evaluation and because he feels that quantity leads to quality. The final rule is that all participants should be encouraged to build upon or modify the ideas of others, "as combinations or modifications of previously suggested ideas often lead to new ideas that are superior to those that sparked them."

We use brainstorming quite often in conjunction with student design projects at Stanford. We frequently ask one of the group to act as recorder, since we have found that a listing of the ideas as they are developed ensures that the group has access to all of its output at all times and also ensures that no ideas are lost. The recording method which works best is one which is large enough in scale (e.g., using felt pens on newsprint or butcher paper or chalk on blackboards) so it is easily readable by everyone in the group. We find that brainstorming works best if the problem is simple and can be well-defined. We find that it works at all levels of problem-solving, from originally attempting to formulate broad concepts to final detail definition.

There are other more behavioral reasons for brainstorming's success, of course. A study group at Harvard looking into brainstorming in the 1950s listed these:

1. Less inhibition and defeatism; rapid fire of ideas presented by the group quickly explodes the myth which the indi-

vidual often casts up that the problem overwhelms him, and that he can't think of a new and different solution
2. Contagion of enthusiasm
3. Development of competitive spirit; everyone wants to top the other's idea

Nonetheless, delay of judgment is probably the most important factor in making brainstorming work.

Brainstorming has at times received a bad name because it was credited with generating ideas which were both shallow and in questionable taste. It has also been heavily spoofed and is sometimes identified with weirdness rather than thoughtfulness. However, the brainstorming process has some solid advantages and, if used when appropriate, is extremely effective. A brainstorming group allows the pooling of a great diversity of background. Shallowness of output is the fault of inadequate information available in the group, poor subsequent judgment, and the leader, not the technique. Brainstorming initially progresses rapidly when it attacks a problem because it is able to utilize common solutions. However, after these are used up, the process becomes more difficult because the members must come up with new concepts. It is in this later period that the technique has the most value. If the session is allowed to stop when the original rush of enthusiasm dies down (due to increased difficulty in thinking of ideas) it will not live up to its potential. The most effective way to learn more about brainstorming is to experience it.

> Exercise: Find a group of people and set up a brainstorming session on a problem which is easily stated in precise terms. Try to think of a problem that is important to all of you. If you cannot, try one of the following:
> 1. Invent some sort of function that would allow you to become friends with a few fascinating people whom you know of, but do not know personally.
> 2. Invent (in reasonable detail) a better way to divide a large (2,000 sq. ft. or so) room into smaller spaces which can be used by various groups. This is an ongoing problem in schools. The dividing system should be flexible (space sizes easily changed), cheap, aesthetically pleasing, and instantly (and easily) changeable.
> 3. Invent an astounding entrée for a far-out dinner party.
> 4. Invent a better way for handling road maps in a car.
> 5. Invent a Christmas greeting card you can mail to your friends which will impress them for all time and let you avoid mailing future cards.

Synectics

Another technique for group problem-solving which has had quite a bit of use is synectics, developed by Synectics Inc., Cambridge, Massachusetts. It is described in detail in the book *Synectics*, by William J.J. Gordon. Although ideation is encouraged, as it is in brainstorming, criticism is not outlawed as rigidly. Synectics also avoids one of the main criticisms aimed at brainstorming—that it begins with answers. Synectics allows the problem definition to be examined in detail. In fact, the main steps in the synectics process are:

Phase 1. Problem as Given
2. Making the Strange Familiar
3. Problem as Understood
4. Operational Mechanisms
5. The Familiar Made Strange
6. Psychological States
7. States Integrated with Problem
8. Viewpoint
9. Solution

The first three of these phases have to do with examining and restating the problem to ensure that it is understood, and with correctly attacking the need. The next two steps involve the use of analogy and metaphor to allow the group to look at the problem in new ways. The remaining phases refer to psychological occurrences that lead the group to a solution.

I cannot go into synectics in full detail here, as it is a rather complex process when compared to brainstorming. Part of its success, in my opinion, stems from its complexity. It essentially tricks a group of problem-solvers into playful thinking by promulgating very tight rules of conduct. It is difficult to walk up to a group of strangers and tell them to think more playfully. However, it is possible to assign the rules and rituals of synectics to them and they will think playfully in such a disciplined way they may not even realize they are doing so.

Perhaps the key to the synectics approach is the use of metaphor. The four operational mechanisms employed in synectics are entitled Personal Analogy, Direct Analogy, Symbolic Analogy, and Fantasy Analogy. The *personal analogy* requires that the problem-solver identify with part or all of the problem and its solution. The *direct analogy* attempts to solve a problem by the direct application of parallel facts, knowledge, technology, or whatever. The *symbolic analogy* is somewhat like the personal analogy, except that the identification is between the problem and objective and impersonal objects or images. The *fantasy analogy* allows the problem-solver to use fantasy to solve the problem.

The best way of showing the use of the operational mechanisms is to quote a passage from Gordon's book. This is a so-called synectics excursion between five people faced with the problem of inventing a vapor-proof closure for space suits. As this passage begins the group has just finished discussing the question, "How do we in our wildest fantasy desire the closure to operate?"

Fantasy Analogy

G: Okay. That's over. Now what we need here is a crazy way to look at this mess. A real insane viewpoint . . . a whole new room with a viewpoint!

T: Let's imagine you could will the suit closed . . . and it would do just as you wanted by wishing . . . (Fantasy Analogy mechanism)

G: Wishing will make it so . . .

F: Ssh, Okay. Wish fulfillment. Childhood dream . . . you wish it closed, and invisible microbes, working for you, cross hands across the opening and *pull* it tight . . .

B. A zipper is kind of a mechanical bug (Direct Analogy mechanism). But not airtight . . . or strong enough . . .

G: How do we build a psychological model of "will-it-to-be-closed"?

R: What are you talking about?

B: He means if we could conceive of how "willing-it-to-be-closed" might happen in an actual model—then we . . .

R: There are two days left to produce a working model—and you guys are talking about childhood dreams! Let's make a list of all the ways there are of closing things.

F: I hate lists. It goes back to my childhood and buying groceries . . .

R: F, I can understand your oblique approach when we have time, but now, with this deadline . . . and you still talking about wish fulfillment.

G: All the crappy solutions in the world have been rationalized by deadlines.

T: Trained insects?

D: What?

B: You mean, train insects to close and open on orders? 1-2-3 Open! Hup! 1-2-3 Close!

F: Have two lines of insects, one on each side of the closure—on the order to close they all clasp hands . . . or fingers . . . or claws . . . whatever they have . . . and then closure closes tight . . .

G: I feel like a kind of Coast Guard Insect (Personal Analogy mechanism).

D: Don't mind me. Keep talking . . .

G: You know the story . . . worst storm of the winter—vessel on the rocks . . . can't use lifeboats . . . some impatient hero grabs the line in his teeth and swims out . . .

B: I get you. You've got an insect running up and down the closure, manipulating the little latches . . .

G: And I'm looking for a demon to do the closing for me. When I will it to be closed (Fantasy Analogy mechanism), Presto! It's closed!

B: Find the insect—he'd do the closing for you!

R: If you used a spider . . . he could spin a thread . . . and sew it up (Direct Analogy mechanism).

T: Spider makes thread . . . gives it to a flea . . . Little holes in the closure . . . flea runs in and out of the holes closing as he goes . . .

G: Okay. But those insects reflect a low order of power . . . When the Army tests this thing, they'll grab each lip in a vise one inch wide and they'll pull 150 pounds on it . . . Those idiot insects of yours will have to pull steel wires behind them in order . . . They'd have to stitch with steel. *Steel* (Symbolic Analogy mechanism).

B: I can see one way of doing that. Take the example of that insect pulling a thread up through the holes . . . You could do it mechanically . . . Same insect . . . put holes in like so . . . and twist a spring like this . . . through the holes all the way up to the damn closure . . . twist, twist, twist, . . . Oh, crap! It would take hours! And twist your damn arm off!

G: Don't give up yet. Maybe there's another way of stitching with steel . . .

B: Listen . . . I have a picture of another type of stiching . . . That spring of yours . . . take two of the . . . let's say you had a long demon that forced its way up . . . like this . . .

R: I see what he's driving at . . .

B: If that skinny demon were a wire, I could poke it up to where, if it got a start, it could pull the whole thing together . . . the springs would be pulled together closing the mouth . . . Just push it up . . . push—and it will pull the rubber lips together . . . Imbed the springs in rubber . . . and then you've got it stitched with steel!

Cross-sectional Diagram

The synectics technique results in a group of people delaying judgment in that they are willing to entertain ideas which normally they would probably reject as impractical. They can do so because the synectics rules tell them to. They are effectively using a technique (like brainstorming) which, temporarily at least, relaxes the watchdog function of the ego and superego and lets the subconscious mind come forth with concepts. These techniques can be used individually as well as within a group, although the synthesis effect of the group will not enter into play. If you happen to think of using a brick as a hot water bottle, the realization that you are making use of the thermal capacity of the brick should quickly spark similar uses (bed warmer, warm floors, luau pit) in your mind just as it would in a group.

But what about ways to alter the ego's regulation of the unconscious mind without such techniques as brainstorming and synectics? Is it possible to somehow relax the control of the ego and superego in general, so that one may make better use of the unconscious mind? The answer is yes, but it is not simple. Let me try to explain the reasons for the difficulty by returning briefly to a discussion of psychology.

As mentioned previously, although there are many theories on the conceptual process to explain various characteristics of conceptualization, complete understanding does not exist. Many psychologists have attempted to explain the mental processes needed in creative thought and the motivations and characteristics of creative people.

Maslow

Abraham Maslow was one of the more significant figures in the attempt to understand creativity. He preferred to talk about "primary" and "secondary" processes rather than about the unconscious and the conscious. Rather than referring to the primary mental process as the unconscious, he called it the "deeper" self, in the sense that it is hidden beneath the surface. Maslow also discussed primary and secondary creativity, as mentioned in Chapter Three. Secondary creativity is that which is evidenced by most people working in a system which requires a great amount of "discipline" work. It utilizes "right-handed" thinking and is based upon breakthroughs (primary creativity) made by others.

To Maslow, primary creativity comes from the deeper or primary self. It is common and universal in children, but in many adults is blocked off to a great extent. In an address called "Creativity in Self-Actualizing People" (contained in *Creativity and Its Cultivation*, edited by Harold Anderson), Maslow discussed a study he did of people who were especially creative and, as he puts it, "self-actualizing." He prefaces his discussion with the admission that very early he abandoned the notion that health, genius, talent, and productivity went together. Maslow found that a great number of people he studied were highly creative in terms of their own self-actualizing capacity, yet were neither particularly productive nor possessors of great "talent" or "genius." He was particularly struck by those people among his subjects who, though they had no noteworthy talent in any area conventionally associated with creativity, were in their daily lives original, novel, ingenious, and inventive. From this, Maslow says he learned to apply the word "creativeness" to many activities, processes, and attitudes other than the standard categories to which the quality is typically ascribed (such as literature, art, theories, etc.). Thus evolved Maslow's distinguishing between "special talent creativeness" (which is typically associated with creativity), and what he calls "self-actualizing creativeness" (primary creativity), which can be manifest in anything we do—in our most ordinary, mundane activities. In studying the traits of self-actualizing people who bring to their everyday affairs an attitude and manner of creativeness, Maslow located certain commonalities. He found these people to be more spontaneous, expressive, and natural and less controlled and inhibited in their behavior than the average. Their behavior seemed less blocked and less self-critical: "This ability to express ideas and impulses without strangulation and without fear of ridicule from others turned out to be an essential aspect of self-actualizing creativeness." Maslow found his subjects to be different from the average person in another way which he felt made creativity more likely: "Self-actualizing people are relatively unfrightened by the unknown, the mysterious, the puzzling, and often are positively attracted by it; i.e., selectively pick it out to puzzle over, to meditate on, and to be absorbed with."

Maslow saw a connection between *creativity in one's actions* and the *inner integration of one's self:* "To the extent that creativeness is constructive, synthesizing, unifying, and integrative, to that extent does it depend in part on the inner integration of the person." Maslow traces this to "the relative absence of fear" found in these subjects—both of others (what they would say, laugh at, demand) and especially of themselves (their insides, impulses, emotions, thoughts). "It was this approval and acceptance of their deeper selves that made it possible to perceive bravely the real nature of the world and also made their behavior more spontaneous (less controlled, less inhibited, less planned, less 'willed,' and designed). By contrast, average and neurotic people walled off, through fear, much that lay within themselves. They controlled, they inhibited, they repressed, and they suppressed. They disapproved of their deeper selves and expected that others did, too." By doing this, Maslow explains, the person "loses a great deal, too, for these depths are also the source of all his joys, his ability to play, to love, to laugh, and, most important for us, to be creative."

Barron

Frank Barron, another psychologist who has done a great deal of research on creativity, takes a slightly different approach. He is unwilling to accept overall psychological health as the criterion for a creative person, because he feels it necessary to formulate criteria which admit to such creative talents as Beethoven, Hooke, Swift, Van Gogh, Rimbaud, Baudelaire, Bronte, Heine, Wagner, and others who created outstanding work in spite of evidence of neuroses, maladjustment, or unhappiness. In an article in *Scientific American*, September 1958, Barron states:

> I would propose the following statements as descriptive of creative artists, and perhaps also of creative scientists:
>
> Creative people are especially observant, and they value accurate observation (telling themselves the truth) more than other people do.
>
> They often express part-truths, but this they do vividly; the part they express is the generally unrecognized; by displacement of accent and apparent disproportion in statement they seek to point to the usually unobserved.
>
> They see things as others do, but also as others do not.
>
> They are thus independent in their cognition, and they also value clearer cognition. They will suffer great personal pain to testify correctly.
>
> They are motivated to this value and to the exercise of this talent (independent, sharp observation) both for reasons of self-preservation and in the interest of human culture and its future.
>
> They are born with greater brain capacity; they have more ability to hold many ideas at once, and to compare more ideas with one another—hence to make a richer synthesis.
>
> In addition to unusual endowment in terms of cognitive ability, they are by constitution more vigorous and have available to them an exceptional fund of psychic and physical energy.
>
> Their universe is thus more complex, and in addition they usually lead more complex lives, seeking tension in the interest of the pleasure they obtain upon its discharge.

They have more contact than most people do with the life of the unconscious, with fantasy, reverie, the world of imagination.

They have exceptionally broad and flexible awareness of themselves. The self is strongest when it can regress (admits primitive fantasies, naive ideas, tabooed impulses into consciousness and behavior), and yet return to a high degree of rationality and self-criticism. The creative person is both more primitive and more cultured, more destructive and more constructive, crazier and saner, than the average person.

Others have hypothesized other models of the creative person, ranging from the happy, well-balanced, suntanned, confident extrovert to the pain-riddled, warped, moody neurotic. Yet, the theme of unguarded unconscious (preconscious or primary self or whatever term we use) surfaces again and again. Therefore let us ask the question: What can we do to free the unconscious from its over-zealous warden?

Psychoanalysis might be an obvious thought, for it is intended to better integrate a personality by making the unconscious more conscious. It supposedly can ameliorate compulsive-obsessive behavior and therefore unlock the primary self. Many psychologists who have studied creativity agree that the goals of psychoanalysts, if reached, should enhance creativity. The fear that psychoanalysis will somehow "ruin" the creative powers of a person has been dismissed by most of the experts. However, for most people, psychoanalysis appears to be somewhat strong medicine for the improvement of creativity. It is expensive, it takes a long time, and its success is not predictable. Psychoanalysis may be attractive if one's behavior is such that life has become acutely unpleasant or unbearable. However, for "normal neurotics" it is perhaps overkill if we're interested in the enhancement of creativity.

Other Paths for Freeing the Unconscious

Are there other ways to free the unconscious? Probably many. Maslow feels that any technique which increases self-knowledge should in principle increase creativity. In the cultures of the Middle and Far East there have existed for many hundreds of years what Robert Ornstein, in his book *The Psychology of Consciousness*, calls "The Traditional Esoteric Psychologies." These have been concerned with personal, empirical approaches to self-knowledge, rather than with impersonal scientific approaches. These psychologies have often developed within disciplines such as Buddhism or Yoga and have utilized techniques such as meditation which are specifically designed to temporarily minimize linear logical thought and strengthen certain mental processes ascribed to the unconscious. Science is just beginning to understand "mystical experiences" and different "levels of consciousness." Ornstein believes that such experiences may be instances where the analytical left side of the brain relinquishes its usual control of consciousness and enables the right side to more freely interpret stimuli in a non-linear, non-deductive way. In his book, Ornstein makes a compelling argument for the integration of such psychologies and techniques with the "right-handed" psychology with which we are familiar. Certainly a higher degree of self-knowledge would result along with an increased respect for "left-handed" thinking. However, these techniques, as practiced in the Middle and Far East, take time and effort, and though they are currently becoming increasingly popular in the Western world, many of us are far from being able and/or willing to use them to improve our conceptual ability.

What paths are easily available to allow us right-handed Westerners to better free the unconscious? Maslow suggests education as one, and I, as an educator rather than a psychiatrist or mystic, must heartily agree. Maslow suspects that although education does little for relieving the repression of "instinct" and "forbidden impulses," it is quite effective in integrating the primary processes and conscious life. Knowledge about the psychological processes, about problem-solving, and especially about one's self can loosen the control of one's ego. The principle involved is a simple one: things are not as threatening when they are understood. Fears are lessened if their sources are understood, and most people's egos are "smart" enough to relax a bit if they are convinced that the results may be positive.

Reading is one of the best ways to gain such self-knowledge. Many books and articles are available concerning the strengthening of one's self-esteem and self-confidence and freeing oneself from unnecessary fears and insecurities. The Reader's Guide section which follows outlines a number of starting points should you desire to journey further, with references to creativity research, psychological theory, and "self-therapy." The books on creativity research will give you a better overview of what is known about creative thinking and the characteristics of highly creative people. Psychological theory books will help you understand human behavior and how the mind works. The "self-therapy" books seek to apply psychological theory in a way in which one can affect one's own behavior.

Understanding the workings of one's mind is somewhat like understanding a golf swing. It allows you to work on changing your present actions in a detailed and conscious way. However, in the case of creative thinking, a side benefit is achieved in gaining a greater understanding of the workings of other people's minds as well. Many fears demand a comparison with other people for their maintenance. The fear of asking questions is often predicated on exposing one's ignorance to others. The fear goes away when one realizes that others are ignorant too. Similarly, one is less afraid of expressing one's emotions when he learns that others have similar emotions, whether they have repressed them or not. Brainstorming works because the other people have silly ideas too. One is more willing to struggle with a problem when it is realized that few people consistently give birth to answers or solutions in a blinding flash of pure inspiration.

Therefore I encourage you to read. The sport of thinking about thinking is an interesting one, and the literature to help you in this pastime is extensive. It can only lead to a better ability to use your own mind—a thorough knowledge of psychological theory and creativity research cannot help but increase your creativity. I feel that we have some effect on the creativity of our students merely by making a "big deal" out of creativity. By elevating it to the status of a class subject and by thus bringing it out of the underground, we cause our students to attach the same importance to it as they do to their other academic subjects and therefore to feel that they should, in fact, be more creative.

Reading, of course, is not the only way to gather knowledge about creativity and conceptualization. You may talk to psychologists and psychiatrists who are involved in trying to give people freer access to their unconscious mind. You may observe those about you and attempt to correlate their actions and their thought processes to their creative output. You may become more introspective about your own thinking (a must in any case) in an attempt to make it more creatively powerful and efficient.

One of the most important activities you should engage in is trying to free your unconscious to engage in creative thinking. If one brainstorms (or synects) or merely *consciously forces oneself to be creative* (by use of lists or whatever), a strange thing happens. First of all, one usually finds that if anything he is more successful in the world, rather than less (so some of one's fears were groundless). He also finds that creative thinking comes easier to him. There are psychological reasons for this. If one uses one's unconscious level, one's consciousness gets the message that such activities are all right. This message is strongly reinforced if some of the outputs from the unconscious result in successes which the ego can revel in. The more creative thinking is done, the more natural and rewarding it becomes and the more the ego relaxes. As a final suggestion on how to somehow relax the guard of the ego and therefore be more creative, I would say:

DO IT!

READER'S GUIDE

As stated previously, there is no complete and scientifically verified explanation of thinking which can result in universal rules for conceptualizing more productively, nor is there likely to be until a much more complete understanding of the mind is available. Still, a great deal of interesting reading exists on this subject with a sizable number of hypotheses, ranging from simplistic to elegant, which shed more light on the creative act. The reading also contains a good bit of conjecture and many value judgments which the reader must sort through and accept or discard depending on whether he is convinced or not (and probably on whether or not the reader's own opinions and values are reinforced).

Be forewarned that my opinion in this area is anything but "the final word." I have often gotten myself into trouble by assigning readings to a class and telling them to skip certain portions because they are of less value. Invariably one (or several) of the students will read these portions (presumably to see *why* they are of less value) and tell me that they are the most important parts of the reading. Therefore take my comments with a grain of salt and spend your effort reading what seems of most value to you.

I am going to give you the names of books, since they are generally more available than papers. Some are in practically all libraries and on the shelves of your local bookstore. Others are more difficult to find. Most of them contain bibliographies of books, papers, and other materials, so you will have no trouble working my few suggestions into an extensive list of future readings.

General Overviews of Creativity and Thinking

First, let me suggest five books on the general subject of creativity which are of vastly different character. The first is *The Art and Science of Creativity* by George F. Kneller (New York: Holt, Rinehart, and Winston, 1965). This is a small and easily read book. It is a good introduction to the subject of creativity, the people in the field, and their discoveries. The first four chapters discuss many existing theories on creativity. The final two chapters contain the author's opinions concerning education and the nature and nurture of creativity.

A relatively large amount of writing on creativity occurred between 1955 and 1965. As an indication of this, in 1964 Taher A. Razik, then with the Creative Education Foundation at the State University of New York at Buffalo (directed by Sidney Parnes), published a bibliography of creative studies which contained 4,176 items, half of which had been written since 1950. There were several national workshops on creative thinking in this period and an established peer group of educators working on the subject. This activity was perhaps in part catalyzed by unhappiness over the conventionality of the 1950s, which gave rise to such critics as Vance Packard, Paul Goodman, and William Whyte—who bemoaned the lack of individuality and inventiveness in society. Many of the people involved in the study of creativity during this period are still active, but the intensity of the work seems to have fallen off somewhat, due to changes in national interest, funding patterns, and the apparent resurgence of individuality (the "do your own thing" philosophy). A good look at the work that was going on in the 1950s and early 1960s is contained in *A Source Book for Creative Thinking*, edited by Sidney J. Parnes and Harold F. Harding (New York: Charles Scribner's Sons, 1962). This book contains a collection of 29 articles and addresses and 75 research summaries. Contributors include Abraham Maslow, Carl Rogers, Alex Osborne, Sidney Parnes, John Arnold, Frank Barron, and other luminaries of creativity study. The book also contains a discussion of bibliographies on creativity available at the time of publication.

One of the most widely quoted books on creativity is *The Act of Creation* by Arthur Koestler (New York: Dell, 1967). Kneller calls *The Act of Creation* "the most ambitious attempt yet made to integrate the findings of a range of disciplines into a single theory of creativity. In this book, bold in its ideas and profusely documented, Koestler seeks to synthesize his own theory of the nature of creativity, as manifested in humor, art, and science, with the latest conclusions of psychology, physiology, neurology, genetics, and a number of other sciences." The book is indeed ambitious *and* successful. It is not light reading. Over 250 articles and books are referenced in the text and contained in the bibliography (an excellent one). It is the type of book which will be read from cover to cover by those deeply interested in conceptualization. Those only mildly interested in conceptualization may never quite finish it, but always think that they should. However, you will benefit from even a partial reading. Another book which contains some excellent articles by major figures in the study of creativity is *Creativity and Its Cultivation*, edited by Harold H. Anderson (New York: Harper & Row, 1959). This volume contains addresses presented at various symposia on creativity held at Michigan State University in 1957 and 1958. Contributors include Erich Fromm, J.P. Guilford, Ernest Hilgard, Rollo May, Margaret Mead, Carl Rogers, Abraham Maslow, and others.

The fifth book on the general subject of creativity is entitled *The Universal Traveler. A Soft-Systems Guidebook to: Creativity, Problem-Solving, and the Process of Design* by Don Koberg and Jim Bagnall. (Los Altos, Calif.: William Kaufmann, Inc., 1974). This book treats the entire problem-solving process, with conceptualization as only part of this. It has a hip, low-budget format and is a delight to read. It contains all manner of hints and warnings to those who travel the path of problem-solving. (Example: As an exercise to combat fear, don't answer your phone the next five times it rings.)

Psychological Theory

Much creativity theory is directly drawn from psychology. Therefore there is a large amount of general psychological literature of interest here. If you have never taken an introductory psychology course (Psychology 1) you should read a good general introductory book to psychology in order to learn the words, the concepts, the names, and the fundamental theories.

A book which I would describe as outstanding is *The Psychology of Consciousness* by Robert E. Ornstein (San Francisco: W. H. Freeman and Company, 1972). This is an up-to-date book which is easily accessible to the lay reader. Ornstein discusses psychology from a "left-brain, right-brain" viewpoint and makes an argument for the integration of conventional psychology, physiology, and what he calls "The Traditional Esoteric Psychologies" (psychologies which treat the "left-handed" aspects of thinking and subjects such as meditation and physiological self-control). Written as an informal textbook, it is well-referenced and well-organized. The bibliography is an excellent reading list for those wanting to learn more about the nature of various states of consciousness.

Two books on the general topic of thinking are *A Study of Thinking* by Jerome S. Bruner, Jacqueline J. Goodnow, and George A. Austin (New York: Wiley, 1957) and *The Nature of Human Intelligence* by J.P. Guilford (New York: McGraw-Hill, 1967). *A Study of Thinking* deals with conceptual aspects of cognition (the means whereby man achieves, retains, and transfers knowledge). It is fairly slow reading, but contains a wealth of material on thinking. It is well referenced and contains an excellent bibliography. The Guilford book contains much discussion on the nature of intelligence and various methods of measuring certain aspects of intelligence. For those of you who like puzzles, it contains examples from psychological texts and speaks about the application of several types of questions in the measuring of intelligence. Of special interest is Guilford's work in defining the various factors which comprise "intelligence."

Another book of interest by Bruner (one of the major contributors to our understanding of the nature of consciousness) is *On Knowing: Essays for the Left Hand* (Cambridge: Harvard University Press, 1966), a collection of writings having to do with the "left-handed" mode of thinking (creativity, discovery, art, literature, myth). Whereas *A Study of Thinking* is quite technical, Bruner's *Essays* are interpretive and delightful reading.

A particularly well-designed treatment of developmental psychology (the development of people from infancy through adulthood) is *Involvement in Developmental Psychology Today* (Del Mar, California: CRM, 1971). The only individuals credited with writing this book are T.G.R. Bower and Robert Merrill Springer, who are listed as contributing consultants. The book contains many illustrations, games, cartoons, and exercises. It is particularly concerned with perception, response to the environment, acculturation, and educational patterns.

If you are a fan of the writing of Erich Fromm, read *The Forgotten Language* (New York: Holt, Rinehart and Winston, 1962). Like most of Fromm's books, it is written with a minimum of referencing, footnoting, and bibliography. However, it is concerned with the unconscious and is a good discussion of symbolic language and dream interpretation. It also compares the theories of Freud and Jung with regard to dream interpretation. If you would like to compare the theories of Freud and Jung yourself, I suggest *On Creativity and the Unconscious* by Sigmund Freud (New York: Harper & Row, 1958) and *Man and His Symbols*, edited by Carl Jung (New York: Doubleday, 1964). The first is a collection of writings by Freud that are concerned with cultural and humanist matters. Many of the selections in the book deal with the particular problems of creative people and reflections upon psychoanalysis and are therefore only marginally pertinent to conceptualization. However, part of the book does treat conceptualization specifically and the book is an interesting insight into some of the lesser-known interests of Freud. *Man and His Symbols* is a translation of Jungian psychology into language accessible to the lay reader. It was put together by Jung and several collaborators during the last years of Jung's life and contains excellent presentations of the principles underlying Jung's thinking and discussions of the nature and importance of man's symbols. It is enjoyable reading. Those of you interested in a broad selection of Freud's writings might enjoy *The Basic Writings of Sigmund Freud*, edited by A.A. Brill (New York: Random House, 1938).

A specific treatment of creativity is found in *Neurotic Distortion of the Creative Process* by Lawrence S. Kubie (New York: Farrar, Straus and Giroux, 1966). Kubie explains the nature of neuroses and creative thought and the interaction between them by use of the concepts of the unconscious, preconscious, and conscious minds. His approach results in a readable and convincing document. A compendium of experimental work having to do with creativity is found in *The Experimental Psychology of Original Thinking* by Wilbert S. Ray (New York: Macmillan, 1967). The book is a summary of pertinent work and contains fifteen selected readings from experimental psychology literature. The book is unfortunately dreary reading for the layman. It reinforces the hypothesis that creative performance can be increased by training and the use of various techniques.

Self-Therapy "How To" Books

There have been several recent paperbacks promulgating a sort of self-therapy approach to psychology. In recent years, there have been major attempts to find approaches to understanding and changing behavior that are more direct and less time-consuming than traditional psychoanalysis. These approaches have all featured a theory (usually not a very scientific one) of behavior and approaches or exercises intended to let one understand and influence his own behavior. I find these books interesting, fun to read and experiment with, and in fact useful in understanding and influencing (in a minor way) my behavior. Do not expect to pick up a paperback at the airport, read it, and thereby shed your neuroses. However, many of these books will at least cause you to think. One worthwhile book is *Gestalt Therapy: Excitement and Growth in the Human Personality* by Frederick Perls, Ralph Hefferline, and Paul Goodman (New York: Dell, 1951). This is a two-volume work. The first volume contains "experiments" which the reader can do to experience the topics which the authors discuss. The second volume is much more technical and much lower on entertainment value. Gestalt therapy itself stresses an "all-at-once" approach, as contrasted with traditional Freudian therapy, which peels away layer-upon-layer seeking the underlying reason for a particular behavior pattern. Two presently popular "fix yourself" books which are available at most news-stands are *Psychocybernetics* by Mathew Maltz (New York: Essendess, 1960) and *I'm O.K., You're O.K.* by Thomas A. Harris (New York: Avon, 1973). I find it beneficial to read books such as these rapidly when I am desperately in need of something to do, as their writing styles leave something to be desired. However, they both have important things to say. The first is a treatment of the importance of self-image. It is well known that one's performance is often a function of one's self-image, a situation which applies in conceptualization as well as in selling, relating to people, or losing weight. *I'm O.K., You're O.K.* is a popularization of Transactional Analysis, which was pioneered by Dr. Eric Berne. The book, by using the classifications of "parent," "adult," and "child" in describing transactional roles in interactions between people, gives the reader a simple perspective from which to view the way in which people relate to one another.

Conceptualization "How To" Books

Let us now look at a few "how to" books on conceptualization. One point of interest here is that many of these have been written by people who were not in the field of psychology. A reasonable explanation of this is found in *The Experimental Psychology of Original Thinking* by Wilbert Ray, who speaks of a "psychology vacuum." He says, "Political scientists postulate something called a power vacuum, which seems to mean that if the most powerful nation in a particular geographical area loses its power, some outside nation will come in and take over control. The same sort of thing happens in psychology. If there is a topic which the psychologists will not, or do not, discuss, someone else will discuss it. . . . This seems to have happened with regard to original behavior."

Two of the more well-known techniques to enhance conceptualization are brainstorming, devised by Alex Osborn, and synectics, devised by Synectics Inc. *Applied Imagination* by Alex Osborn (New York: Charles Scribner's Sons, 1953) discusses not only brainstorming, but also Osborn's thinking about creativity. It is written in an expansive, early 1950s style and tends to reference opinion rather than science, but it strikes a responsive chord in some readers (I am not one of them). It was quite influential, as was Osborn himself, in the upsurge in the study of creativity in the 1950s. *Synectics* by William J.J. Gordon (New York: Harper & Row, 1961) talks about the history of the Synectics Research Group in Cambridge, Mass., the technique of synectics, and its application. It is a mixture of technique and of philosophy. Synectics is a particularly interesting technique because of its emphasis on metaphorical thinking. It is also of interest because it has been tried by a number of large corporations in problem-solving. The book is easy to read and entertaining. I should add that *Synectics* has an extensive bibliography, which contains some 300 entries on a wide variety of subjects. Its disadvantage as a bibliography is that it is so general that it gives no indication to the reader of what to expect from the various entries. However, it is definitely an interesting reading list.

If you were interested in the list of problem-solving strategies in Chapter Five, *Tools for Change* (San Francisco: Interaction Associates, 1971) might appeal to you. It is concerned with the proper use of thinking strategies, or "heuristics," in problem-solving. Although primarily written for educators it contains concepts of interest to everyone. This book is not distributed through bookstores, but can be purchased from Interaction Associates in San Francisco. *New Think* by Edward de Bono (New York: Basic Books, 1967) espouses the virtues of lateral thinking. He defines vertical thinking as careful logical analysis that concentrates on reaching an answer from the given data. Lateral thinking is "sideways" thinking, which utilizes different viewpoints and different approaches to come up with new ideas and fresh approaches. It is a well-written, engaging, and convincing book.

An outstanding "how to" book is *Experiences in Visual Thinking* by Robert McKim (Monterey: Brooks/Cole, 1972). This book not only goes deeply into imagery in a very effective and experiential way, but also contains generous discussion of conceptualization, drawing, and general problem-solving. It is an excellently designed book with plenty of illustrations, puzzles, experiments, and problems. It is used as a text in an extremely popular undergraduate course at Stanford (Viz-Think in the local jargon) and is a convincing argument for the importance of visual thinking. It is fun to read and deceptively profound.

Visual Thinking by Rudolf Arnheim (Berkeley: University of California Press, 1969) is an elegantly written and more theoretical argument for the importance of visual thinking. Arnheim is a prolific and scholarly writer, and this volume is probably soon to become a classic among those who are involved in the visual world. Another book concerned with imagery is *The Intelligent Eye* by R.L. Gregory (New York: McGraw-Hill, 1970). This book discusses perception and imagery. It is well illustrated with examples in both two and three dimensions (red and green 3-D glasses included). It should be especially appealing to those of you who are fascinated by optical illusions.

Two books which are also often quoted in literature on creativity have to do with qualitative studies of creative people. *The Creative Process*, edited by Brewster Ghiselin (New York: Mentor, 1963) is a collection of writings by extremely creative people (Mozart, Einstein, Poincaré, etc.). These letters speak to the creative process used by the writers. They cover many phenomena (such as Mozart's ability to hear music and then simply write it down) that are folklore among those who treat creativity in educational establishments. *An Essay on the Psychology of Invention in the Mathematical Field* by Jacques Hadamard (New York: Dover, 1954) is a study of creativity among outstanding mathematicians and scientists. It is an attempt by a mathematician to explain mathematical and scientific invention.

As a final suggestion, for those of you who like puzzles and games, look in the mathematical section of your libraries. Mathematicians have a soft spot for such pastimes. There is even a *Journal of Recreational Mathematics*, put out by the Baywood Publishing Co. Most puzzle and game books cater to a wide range of mathematical prowess. A few of the better ones are: *Mathematical Teasers* by Julio A. Mira (New York: Barnes & Noble Inc., 1970); *Mathematical Games* by C. Lukács and E. Tarján, translated by John Dobai (New York: Walker and Co., 1968); *The Magic of Numbers* by Sydney H. Lamb (New York: Arc Books Inc., 1967); *The Unexpected Hanging and Other Mathematical Diversions* by Martin Gardner, editor of the Mathematical Games Department of *Scientific American* magazine (New York: Simon and Schuster, 1969); *536 Puzzles and Curious Problems* by Henry Ernest Dudeney, edited by Martin Gardner (New York: Charles Scribner's Sons, 1967); and *Martin Gardner's Sixth Book of Mathematical Games*, from *Scientific American* (San Francisco: W.H. Freeman and Co., 1971). Even if you are uncomfortable around mathematics, you should still find material in such books that will keep you off the streets for a while.

ABOUT THE AUTHOR

PROFESSOR JAMES L. ADAMS is director of the Stanford School of Engineering's Design Division, a group noted for its innovative approach to teaching, its attention to the emotional and intellectual aspects of design as well as the physical, and its concern with the problem-solving process. Professor Adams is particularly interest in the initial phases of design and the interplay between aesthetic and technical considerations in design. He is originally from Southern California and received his BS degree from California Institute of Technology and his graduate degrees from Stanford. He also spent a period of time as an art student at UCLA, served a tour in the Air Force, and held several part-time jobs in design and development before receiving his PhD and, in his words, "leaving school forever again."

Professor Adams was employed by the Jet Propulsion Laboratory in Pasadena, California, from 1960 until 1966, where he was involved in the design of the first Venus and Mars spacecraft, several feasibility studies, and the supervision of advanced development groups. In 1966 he returned to Stanford as a faculty member. He has written many articles in the areas of engineering education, spacecraft design, and remote control, and is considered to be one of the outstanding teachers in the Engineering School. He lives on the campus with his wife, Gretchen, and his sons, Bob and Dan.